"Oh, No You Don't!" Clete Exclaimed.

His hand reached out to grasp her slender wrist. "You're not going to run away from me anymore! I want you, Miranda, I always have."

"Want is not love!" Miranda cried defiantly, wrenching herself away from his firm grip.

"And who says I don't love you?"

Miranda's heart skipped several beats before she could answer. "Don't, Clete. I can't live a lie anymore." Her voice was low and sounded strange to her own ears. "It takes two to make a marriage work. . . ."

MIA MAXAM

was born and raised in Europe in a U.S. Air Force family. She and her two daughters have recently moved to Anchorage, Alaska for a three year stint with her U.S. Air Force husband. Mia's many talents include photography and writing. She maintains a lifelong interest in history and language.

Dear Reader:

I'd like to take this opportunity to thank you for all your support and encouragement of Silhouette Romances.

Many of you write in regularly, telling us what you like best about Silhouette, which authors are your favorites. This is a tremendous help to us as we strive to publish the best contemporary romances possible.

All the romances from Silhouette Books are for you, so enjoy this book and the many stories to come. I hope you'll continue to share your thoughts with us, and invite you to write to us at the address below:

Karen Solem
Editor-in-Chief
Silhouette Books
P.O. Box 769
New York, N.Y. 10019

MIA MAXAM
Lost in Love

Silhouette Romance

Published by Silhouette Books New York

America's Publisher of Contemporary Romance

Other Silhouette Books by Mia Maxam

Race the Tide

SILHOUETTE BOOKS, a Division of Simon & Schuster, Inc.
1230 Avenue of the Americas, New York, N.Y. 10020

Distributed by Pocket Books

ISBN: 0-671-57236-9

First Silhouette Books printing July, 1983

10 9 8 7 6 5 4 3 2 1

Map by Ray Lundgren

SILHOUETTE, SILHOUETTE ROMANCE and colophon are
registered trademarks of Simon & Schuster, Inc.

America's Publisher of Contemporary Romance

Printed in the U.S.A.

Lost in
Love

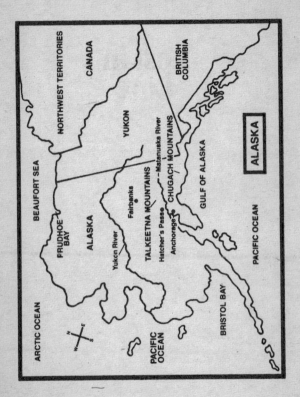

ALASKA

ARCTIC OCEAN

BEAUFORT SEA

NORTHWEST TERRITORIES

CANADA

PRUDHOE BAY

ALASKA

YUKON

BRITISH COLUMBIA

Yukon River

Fairbanks

TALKEETNA MOUNTAINS

Matanuska River

Hatcher's Pass

CHUGACH MOUNTAINS

Anchorage

GULF OF ALASKA

PACIFIC OCEAN

BRISTOL BAY

PACIFIC OCEAN

N W E S

Chapter One

As the elevator doors opened silently on the twenty-ninth floor of the Texbridge Oil Building in downtown Houston, a petite, brown-haired woman stepped out with even, efficient steps. Her unfaltering stride took her down the thickly carpeted corridor that led to the office of the company's president, George Bridger. Miranda Bridger paid little attention to the elegant surroundings that bespoke of the firm's overt prosperity. Her mind, as usual, was on the latest geological report. Its findings were even more than what she had been hoping for, and that was why she had returned from her trip early. She felt almost elated as she eagerly thought of her father's pleasure when she showed him the thick file she carried possessively in the crook of her left arm. In her right hand she clasped a thick, expensive-looking envelope. She had brought it along almost as an afterthought, giving it only cursory notice after its initial arrival.

Miranda was George Bridger's only child and she had been raised in an opulent world where "price per barrel" and "exchange commodities" were words used every day. Later her interests were channeled into the scientific aspects of the oil industry. Five years worth of college had been crammed into three years of intensive study, and at the tender age of twenty-one, Miranda Bridger had earned a master's degree in petroleum engineering. She had graduated with the highest honors, and had immediately gone to work for her father's company in Houston, Texas. That had been four years ago.

Too many people had been·skeptical about her business expertise when they discovered her father owned the company for which she worked. They did not realize her father was her greatest critic and that she was continuously having to prove her worth to the powerful George Bridger. If she had been born the son he had always wanted, it wouldn't have been necessary, but, as she had often heard him lament, Miranda was "regretfully" his sole heir.

Since it was not yet seven o'clock in the morning, the corridors of the twenty-ninth floor were deserted. But the fresh aroma of coffee alerted Miranda that Sean Williams, her father's male secretary, was somewhere about. She sniffed appreciatively and altered her steps toward the coffeepot located in a small, out-of-sight alcove.

She put down the folder of highly valuable geological data, depositing the other envelope on top of the bulging file. Then she poured a cup of the rich brew and savored its flavor as she absently pondered the thick envelope containing a slender, gold-embossed box. Dayton would be pleased to see it, she thought, never once wondering why she experienced a lack of similar emotion.

As she took another sip of the satisfying coffee, Miranda heard voices coming from the side entrance to her father's private office. Scooping up the folder and with the envelope balanced precariously on top, she made her way toward the partly opened door. She grimaced as the envelope slid off its resting place, the coffee cup in her right hand preventing her from catching it as it fell silently to the carpet. Setting the coffee aside, Miranda knelt quickly to retrieve the envelope before Dayton caught her being so careless. She could hear his deep laugh through the door that stood ajar, and his words caught her attention.

"I'm glad Charlene liked Sandra. It meant a lot to me, George."

"She seems like fun, Day, just what a man needs from time to time, eh?" George replied. The uncharacteristic teasing quality in her father's voice surprised Miranda.

"Shall I send both ladies the standard dozen red roses, then, sir?" Sean's voice joined the other two.

"Yes, but first get me the real estate file on Charlene's place, Sean. She's been nagging me about getting the deed to her house put in her name." George sounded mildly rueful. "This is what it always comes to, Day. Women want more and more until the time comes for the big payoff. Wife or mistress, it makes no difference in the long run."

"I don't know of any woman who's ever gotten the upper hand with you, George," Dayton replied admiringly. "Just look what all of Barbara's pleas got her."

Miranda's head jerked up involuntarily at the mention of her mother, whom she had not seen for nearly seven years.

"May I remind you that the divorce settlement I made on Barbara was very generous."

"Generous as far as money goes, but I always maintained that the stipulation that Barbara never approach Miranda was a little harsh." Behind the door, Miranda could hardly believe Dayton's words. She held her breath, afraid, yet compelled to listen further.

"It's a harsh world out there, Day, and you know it. If Barbara ever makes a move to see Miranda, she knows I'll ruin that lawyer husband of hers. He'd never be able to stand up under the pressure from Texbridge, and I'd fix it so no corporate law firm would ever hire him again!"

"You act as if Barbara left you for Miles, George," Day chided, "when in truth it was Barb's discovery of Charlene's existence that set off the whole thing." Dayton Green was the only person who could speak so bluntly to George Bridger and get away with it.

George responded with a harsh laugh. "She should have kept looking the other way, just as Miranda will when she starts suspecting something between you and Sandra!"

Miranda could only listen with amazement at the conversation between her father and her fiancé.

"I don't want to give up Sandra!" Dayton exclaimed and Miranda detected an uncharacteristic note of passion in his voice. "But I don't want to give up Miranda either!"

"Meaning you don't want to risk losing all that stock in Texbridge that I'll transfer solely in your name on the day you marry my daughter!" George taunted Dayton, the blunt words shocking Miranda as she hid in the next room.

"You've admitted often enough yourself, George, that your daughter is like a machine, a cool, intellectual woman with a brain like an elegant computer!"

"That shouldn't present a problem to you, Day. With all your expertise with women, you should be able to melt some of that ice," George jeered.

"Never—your daughter is too entrenched in her job to ever put me first. She's like you in that respect, George. All business. Her blood is as thick as the oil that's made you rich! The only thing that excites her is a fresh geological report!" Miranda glanced guiltily down at the folder she still gripped in her hand, the knuckles white from pressure. "She just won't let herself be a real woman—even her hairstyle and clothes, why she looks the prim and proper miss complete with reading glasses pushed up over her head, her hair tied into a tight knot, always wearing suits instead of dresses." Miranda's hand moved upward to her no-nonsense hairstyle, her sleek brown hair French-braided around her face, the remainder of it drawn tightly into a neat roll at her nape.

"And the few times I've tried to get Miranda to go to bed with me," Dayton continued, "she froze up even more than her usual self! I often wonder what I'm getting myself into, George."

"But, Day, think of all the power you'll wield after your marriage!" Miranda's father taunted his executive assistant even more, as if he gloried in controlling every aspect of Dayton Green's future. "You'll be able to afford keeping a dozen Sandras," he added cruelly.

Miranda felt sick to her stomach. She straightened with great difficulty and grasped the envelope tightly in her hands. It contained the invitations to Houston's wedding of the year, the marriage of Texbridge heiress Miranda Bridger to upcoming tycoon Dayton Green.

As if in a fog, Miranda noted that Sean Williams had retrieved a folder from the filing cabinet and was back in her father's office. She took advantage quickly and forced herself to move her frozen body. With the papers clutched tightly to her chest, she moved jerkily over the carpeting, careful not to make a telltale noise as she opened the heavy door to the outer hallway. The elevator felt stifling, but thankfully, the trip to her office, many floors below, was quick. As she entered the modest cubbyhole that had been assigned to her in the engineering department, she was amazed to see from her digital clock that a mere fifteen minutes had passed since she had left. How much her life had been changed in such a short period of time!

Everything she had overheard kept whirling around in her mind, but as she paced back and forth in the small area, she sifted out the important facts, ordering them in her analytical mind. She felt as if she had been living a lie for the past seven years, since she had last seen her socially prominent mother, in fact. She felt ashamed of all the cruel things she had flung at Barbara, but at the time Miranda had only believed her father's side of the story. He had told her that her mother did not care about her, and like a fool, Miranda had believed the mighty George Bridger! Her well-bred mother had never once mentioned the existence of another woman in Miranda's father's life.

Obviously Dayton had known the truth, too. He was a good fifteen years older than Miranda, and she had been attracted to him because he was so much like her father. Better yet, her father had approved of their match. Miranda had been convinced that Dayton loved her, she had been convinced that she had been more than just another woman to him. Now she realized it was not love, but her "dowry" of stock in Texbridge that had drawn him to her. Remembering the passion in his voice as he spoke of his mistress, Miranda was sure that Dayton was in love with Sandra.

Suddenly all the frustration and hurt she had suffered at overhearing the conversation between the two most important men in her life overwhelmed her. With unaccustomed temper, she took the expensive-looking envelope filled with wedding invitations and threw it forcefully into the wastebasket beside her desk. It hit with a resounding thud.

She stared down at her reading glasses lying on the desk. As she recalled Dayton's disparaging remark about her appearance, the glasses followed the wedding invitations into the basket.

She had to get out of the building! She must think about the situation she now faced. All her life, she had had a definite direction; everything had been mapped out so clearly. But now everything had changed and she felt at loose ends.

The fresh morning air was reviving to her body and spirit. She walked with quick, fluid steps through the streets of the awakening city, dwelling inwardly on the hurt and betrayal she felt. Eventually she found herself in front of the building where her penthouse apartment was located. By the time she entered the cool, comfortable interior, Miranda had

a resolute grasp on herself and knew clearly what she
wanted to do.

A scant hour later, one small suitcase in hand and
all her savings in her expensive handbag, Miranda
found herself at the Houston airport. She walked
determinedly over the cool, tiled floor of the airport
lobby to the nearest ticket counter, not caring which
airline she chose. From the video screen mounted
overhead, she saw that the next flight out was leaving
shortly. Flight 95, the monitor read.

"Give me a ticket on 95."

"All the way?" the young man inquired. He threw
her a skeptical look, taking in her conservative, but
elegant appearance in one sweeping glance.

"Yes, please."

"That flight is in the process of boarding right
now, miss. You'll have to hurry to make it." He
shook his head as if he thought it was already too
late to catch it.

Miranda quickly paid the man in cash and, with
his hurried instructions in mind, she ran down the
concourse to the boarding gate, her suitcase gripped
tightly in one hand, the strap of her handbag secured
over her shoulder. She was the last person to board
and the stewardess closed the door immediately
after Miranda's breathless entrance.

By the time the plane circled their first stop,
Dallas, Miranda had written two cryptic notes, one
for Dayton to break their engagement and one for
her boss to give her resignation. One of the stewards
kindly offered to see that the letters were posted.

It was not yet noon in Dallas, but the sun high
overhead was brilliantly reflected off a multitude of
points, dazzling the eye. Miranda had been in Dallas

many times since Texbridge had corporate offices here, too. The vacated seats on the plane were filling up rapidly with new boarders. The curtain separating the first class section had been drawn back, and Miranda could see it was almost filled. She was anxious for the plane to get underway. Hurry up and wait, Miranda thought wryly.

A distinguished-looking man with silver hair was speaking to the stewardess, his head bent low, his profile revealing a hawklike nose. With sudden dismay Miranda realized she knew the man well. He was vice president of Operations and Engineering in their Dallas offices! Pace Dickinson often had dinner at the Bridger mansion outside of Houston. If he saw her, she'd have a hard time explaining what she was doing there, and he would in all probability insist that she join him up front. And worse than that, he would eventually mention to her father or to Dayton where he had seen her, and from there, it would be easy for them to trace her whereabouts. Realizing more than ever how ruthless her father could be, Miranda definitely did not want the man to see her. Quickly, she slid over to the window seat.

Almost immediately the seat she had just left was taken by a young airman in Air Force blues. Miranda turned her head to the window, hoping desperately that Pace would not discover her presence. Exactly where was this flight going? she wondered for the first time. She had paid scant attention to its ultimate destination, not caring in the least where fate led her.

When she pulled her ticket from her handbag, she saw that she was booked to Prudhoe Bay, Alaska. The North Slope! No wonder the ticket agent had looked at her so strangely. Ironically she had board-

ed the "Pipeline Express," the most likely flight
possible to run into people in the oil business!

Miranda shook her head at her luck as she leaned
back wearily in her seat, her mind busy on what she
should do next. The silver-haired man in first class
was probably going all the way to the North Slope.
According to the brochure, the aircraft made stops
in Seattle, Anchorage and Fairbanks before it
reached its final destination.

In Seattle, Miranda readied herself to walk boldly
past Dickinson. As luck would have it, just as she
was ready to leave, he became engaged in conversation with an attractive stewardess. He was facing the
aisle that she would have to traverse to exit the
plane, the two of them effectively blocking her
escape. There was no way she could avoid coming
face to face with him. Feeling like a fugitive, Miranda sighed and turned her attention to the view from
her window, resigned that she would have to maneu-
ver a successful exit at their next stop. She stared out
at the gloomy overcast skies that predictably blan-
keted Washington's northwest coast.

In definite contrast, the skies over Anchorage
were clear and, as the aircraft circled, Miranda could
see the velvety green mountains surrounding the city
below them. It had seemed like a long flight, and
when another meal had been served along with
another miniature bottle of California wine, Miranda had drank more than she had eaten. As the craft
touched ground, she felt slightly dizzy. The airman
next to her leaned forward eagerly to see the area
where he'd be living for the next year. As the plane
taxied to a stop, the aisles filled quickly with passen-
gers eager to step onto land.

"Well, this is where I leave—" The airman had been trying to capture Miranda's attention throughout the long flight.

The interior of the plane seemed chaotically crowded as many prepared to depart. She decided that this could be her last chance to slip off unnoticed so, with a beguiling smile, she stood up.

"Me, too," she murmured to her companion, looking up at him expectantly. She felt strangely light-headed and grabbed at the back of the seat for support.

"Can I help?" he offered, concerned yet delighted with Miranda's sudden change of attitude. At her request, he retrieved her small suitcase. She should never have drunk the wine, unaccustomed as she was to alcohol, she thought as she watched him.

"Tell me about the job you'll be doing at the base," she encouraged the airman, as she kept close beside him. To a casual observer they appeared to be traveling together and, as the young man eagerly explained the ups and downs of being an aircraft mechanic working in a cold-weather location, Miranda slipped successfully past Pace Dickinson, who had remained in his seat, paying little attention to the departing crowd.

Inside the terminal she allowed the airman to lead her down the escalator. "I have to get my bags," he told her as he took hold of her elbow to assist her off the electric staircase. The crowd from Flight 95 was congregating around the baggage pickup area. "Can I get the rest of yours?" he asked politely.

"No, this is all I have," Miranda answered.

"Will you wait?" His blue eyes were hopeful and Miranda hated to disillusion him. After all, he had been very helpful. As the airman left her side, she turned to find the silver-haired man standing across the room. He looked directly at her. Even at that distance, Miranda could see a hesitant glimmer of recognition flicker over Dickinson's face. She panicked as he made a move toward her.

With a tight grip on her suitcase, she rushed toward the exit doors that opened automatically for her. Her head felt as if it were stuffed with cotton. Did someone call out her name? Only Pace knew who she really was, for she hadn't given anyone else her name. Feeling better outside in the crisp northern air, she hurried along the sidewalk that ran parallel to the loading zone. She felt ridiculous fleeing from the man like this. Yet she knew full well how ruthless her father could be when things didn't go his way, and she felt justified in doing anything to avoid detection. If she escaped now, Pace would most likely brush the incident off as a case of mistaken identity and think no more about it.

A silver and blue bus had pulled up ahead of the line of cars and taxis, drawing close to the curb with a noisy hiss of air brakes. As its doors opened, Miranda veered toward it and stepped in quickly before Pace, standing with his back to her at the exit, could see where she had gone.

Safely inside the bus, she took a deep breath to clear her head and rested her suitcase on the top step. The driver eyed her with a tired look.

"This is a charter, lady, and you don't look like you're a member of the Tokyo Realtor Association." His voice was dry with humor.

"Would you believe me if I told you I was their tour guide?" She raised an eyebrow hopefully.

"Nice try." He shook his head. "I do this run four times a year and you don't look anything like Yashimoto."

"A male guide, huh?"

"Yup."

"Well, would you mind if I just caught my breath for a second?" Every time she bent over, the scene in front of her eyes tilted crazily.

"Just for a second. See that crowd coming out of the exit? That's them!"

Miranda was elated. The excited group from Tokyo was between her and Pace Dickinson from Dallas! Quickly she took off her jacket, folding it away in a side pocket of her case; she loosened the buttoned collar of the chiffon blouse. As her fingers touched the tight roll of hair at her nape, she remembered once more Dayton's remarks about her appearance and, more specifically, her hairstyle. She pulled at the pins holding the knot secure and slid off the elastic band. Her rich brown hair cascaded down her back and over her shoulders in a shiny mass. The driver observed her with new interest and his admiring gaze told her that the change in her appearance was more than effective.

"Well, have fun!" she told him. "Here they come!" And here I go, she told herself, sucking in a deep breath as she plunged down the steps of the bus. The crowd of Japanese tourists hid her well and, undetected, she slipped around the front of the bus.

Traffic had rapidly increased, probably due to several arrivals in a relatively short period of time. She crossed the lanes of traffic to wind her way through several rows of vehicles. She glanced over her shoulder several times to see where Pace had gone. Miranda was beginning to feel paranoid. There he was, in the process of turning toward her now! There was no doubt he would see her.

A long black limousine was parked at the curb in front of her, its tinted windows dark. From her vantage point its interior appeared unoccupied. Impulsively, Miranda opened the back door and slid in quickly, dragging her suitcase in behind her. As she closed the door, she stared back at Pace through the dark glass. He hadn't seen her. She sighed, and with relief she sank back into the soft, luxurious upholstery of the quiet interior.

A slight movement to her left caught her attention immediately. She wasn't alone in the car! At that realization, her heart skipped several beats. Miranda turned to see an expensively dressed elderly lady staring at her with the most piercing eyes she had ever encountered. The woman moved a frail-looking hand to a place over her heart. Afraid she had unduly frightened the lady, Miranda hastened to apologize and explain her rash entry.

"Oh, I hope I didn't frighten you, slipping in here unannounced—" She leaned toward the woman anxiously.

"No . . . no, of course you didn't, my dear," the gray-haired woman replied graciously. "I'm made of sterner stuff than I look, for heaven's sake!" She laughed quickly, as if to convince Miranda.

"Well, I have to admit, you're taking all this much better than I would have in your place." Miranda looked the woman over carefully, intensely relieved that she apparently hadn't done this frail-looking person any lasting damage.

"Oh, you have years yet before you're in my

situation, my dear, but I'm sure you'll do just fine when the time comes."

As she wondered at the strange comment, Miranda decided to humor the old lady and could only say, "Thank you, thank you so much for being so kind and understanding to a stranger. I feel I owe you at least some sort of explanation. You see . . ."

The woman interrupted her before Miranda could say more. "Oh, you don't have to explain. I know all about the ups and downs of love! You young people—you all think your situation is so unique, so different from anything that ever happened to anyone else. But let me tell you, there's not one feeling, not one situation, that hasn't occurred before to someone else at one time or another down the ages! So you don't have to explain anything to me, my dear." The woman reached out and patted Miranda's hand comfortingly.

What was the old lady talking about? Could she look into Miranda's soul and see all the hurt and resentment there? Or was what happened to her so obvious that anyone could read it plainly on her face?

"Then my coming here like this hasn't upset you?" She wanted to be reassured that the woman was taking her intrusion as well as she insisted she was.

"No, no . . . and you're so lovely . . ."

In her anxiety, Miranda did not hear the door beside her open and did not notice that another person had joined them until she felt the cushion sag under the added weight. The old lady peered past Miranda and smiled.

"Oh, Clete, I was just going to tell your wife that she's much lovelier than I had even imagined. Her voice on the telephone yesterday certainly didn't do her justice."

Thoroughly confused, Miranda turned in her seat to better observe the newcomer, Clete. Her eyes met his. He was so close that her breath caught in her throat. He was just as confused by the old lady's words as Miranda was.

Thick black lashes framed a pair of brown eyes that caught Miranda's gaze immediately, holding her prisoner. Curiosity, admiration, male interest, all flashed in the man's eyes quickly, his sharp, intelligent gaze taking in everything about her in the space of a moment. From his superior height, he looked down at Miranda, and slowly, a grin spread across the stern, good-looking face as if he had read something in her captured look. She felt as if he knew her every thought, as if he knew her innermost secrets.

The wide smile touching well formed masculine lips made the formidably handsome man look boyishly appealing. His eyes continued to hold Miranda's gaze with an intimacy that disconcerted her. His closeness and the refreshing scent of his distinctive cologne added to the feeling.

"No, Mother," he answered slowly as if the situation had become clear to him. "Mere words alone would never be enough to do this lady justice." His bold look swept over her feminine figure in the gauzy blouse that she suddenly remembered was wantonly unbuttoned to show the cleavage between her thrusting breasts. Miranda was conscious of the man's undisguised interest in her womanly attributes.

She flushed becomingly under his honest scrutiny of her figure, and the old lady, his mother, if

Miranda had understood correctly, laughed with delight.

"Clete, shame on you! You've made her blush. It reassures me, though, that you haven't broken with old-fashioned traditions." She turned to Miranda. "It's wonderful to know that girls with principles still exist, my dear. And Clete, you must treasure such a find, son—such women are rare!" The old lady's eyes sparkled with a strange light.

"Indeed, Mother, indeed . . ." He took Miranda's icy hand in his, the strong feel of his warm clasp strangely reassuring. It was disconcerting, feeling like this toward a complete stranger, but Miranda knew instinctively that she could trust this dark-haired man sitting next to her. As if once more reading her mind, he gave her hand a surreptitious squeeze. Then he stretched his other arm around her shoulders and pulled her close to him on the seat. His mouth was close to her ear, his breath stirring the tendrils of curls at her temple. A shiver of something she could not define danced along her spine.

"It's okay, really," he murmured, his voice so low that only she could hear it. His mother beamed happily at the couple. Miranda turned her head to glance over Clete's shoulder out the window. Pace was crossing the street, apparently still looking for her. She was much safer in the limousine, Miranda realized, safer in the company of these two people, one of whom seemed to think she was someone else.

The front door of the vehicle opened and a liveried chauffeur slipped into the driver's seat. He turned toward the two younger people in the back seat to smile widely at Miranda.

"Welcome to your new home, Mrs. Montana. I

hope you'll be happy here. The staff and I are eagerly looking forward to helping you settle in and, as a token of our best wishes and regards, we took the liberty of bringing you a bridal bouquet." He handed her a large bouquet of white, long-stemmed roses interspersed with baby's breath and delicate green fern.

Miranda found the exquisite flowers thrust onto her lap, the heady scent of roses assailing her dazed senses. She should never have drunk that wine!

"The lady is speechless, Adam," Clete Montana answered, a devilish quirk lifting one corner of his strong mouth. Miranda's gaze moved from Adam to Clete. The attractive cleft in the rather stubborn chin fascinated her.

Clete's mother seemed pleased with Miranda's mute astonishment at the bouquet. "We should be on our way," she told the chauffeur. She turned toward her son. "Did Adam tell you that everyone is waiting at the house for your appearance?"

Clete nodded rather grimly, and Miranda could feel his figure stiffening as he held her close to his side. She had the definite feeling that the idea of a wedding reception did not please him.

"The reception is probably in full swing by now! Everyone is so anxious to meet your lovely bride. Joyce is acting as hostess until we arrive. I hope you don't mind crowds." She looked pointedly at Miranda. "But of course you wouldn't. In your profession, you must be accustomed to it."

The car moved effortlessly onto a highway leading away from the airport. For a moment Miranda almost panicked, but the comforting man beside her murmured soothingly, "Don't worry, you'll be all right." His warm hand continued to hold hers, and she relaxed somewhat.

Clete's mother kept up a running dialogue. The excitement brought color to her frail-looking face, and more than once Miranda caught Clete throwing his mother a worried glance.

"This is all so romantic." She sighed, settling herself comfortably beside Miranda. The old lady looked so tiny and vulnerable, Miranda thought as she listened with interest to the other woman's tale.

"So romantic," she continued, "you and Clete meeting again after so many years, and then practically eloping in Las Vegas yesterday!" Miranda was beginning to put the pieces of the puzzle together. She looked up at Clete through the safety of her sable dark eyelashes, but he caught her glance. His mouth twisted in an ironic smile, one eyebrow turning upward at the movement.

"I wouldn't even have known about it if I hadn't called Clete about some business matters yesterday. It's fortunate I talked to you, my dear, because I'm convinced Clete would never had said a word! But what a nuisance, to have your future mother-in-law call in the middle of your elopement!" She chuckled with delight.

Could this man have possibly been jilted at the altar, Miranda speculated with wonder, jilted at the very last moment? What woman would give up a chance at being a wife to such a magnificent man? She admired his shoulders, broad and powerful beneath a well-cut summer suit of beige linen. His hair was the color of a raven's wing, his skin tanned to a complementary gold that emphasized his healthy countenance. He was trim and fit, his legs

lean with latent strength that was visible where the
material of his slacks hugged their long length. His
clothes were expensive, but not ostentatious.

These thoughts took a mere instant and Miranda
returned her attention to his mother's monologue.

"I don't know if Clete ever told you, but his father
and I had a whirlwind courtship, marrying scarcely
one month after we met! And we had forty wonderful years together. Clete is very like his father, too;
once he falls in love, he'll be faithful forever. He'd
never let anything come between him and the
woman he'll cherish for life, and beyond . . ." Her
voice trailed away, her thoughts obviously in the
past.

Miranda stared at the old lady, all the pieces of the
puzzle suddenly becoming crystal clear in her befuddled mind. Why, she thinks I'm her new daughter-
in-law, and of course, under the circumstances,
Miranda could fully understand how she could make
the mistake. She had been expecting a young woman's arrival, and when Miranda had slipped into the
limousine, she had naturally assumed the stranger
was her son's new wife!

But her son, Clete . . . Why wasn't he setting his
mother straight? Miranda wondered. And where
was the absent bride, the new Mrs. Montana whom
this man should have just married? Not risking the
scrutiny of those mesmerizing brown eyes again,
Miranda contented herself with gazing at his strong,
capable hand that continued to grip hers. It was a
hand that calmed her, reassured her, a hand capable
of a tender touch, and a vision of that hand caressing
her palm, her wrist, moving upward to her shoulder
came unbidden to her wandering thoughts. The
touch of that masterful hand could melt her bones.

Miranda flushed as the elderly Mrs. Montana interrupted her intimate thoughts with a question.

"I do hope you won't miss the glamor and glitter of Las Vegas, my dear. You've led such a colorful life!" Clete's mother peered over at Miranda nestled closely in her son's arms. "I have to admit, though, you're a lot younger than you sounded on the phone. Oh, I hope you don't mind my frankness!"

"No, no, of course not! I welcome the truth!" With those words she raised innocent-looking eyes to Clete's face, and he smiled ever so slightly. They understood each other.

The limousine rolled on through the city, but Miranda had no eyes for the gleaming skyline or the new spring green of the countryside, evidence that summer came late to this great northland.

"Where are we going?" Miranda asked in a low voice that only Clete Montana could hear. His mother had fallen silent, perhaps becoming a little tired from all of the excitement.

"To my home," came the low answer in the man's pleasantly deep voice, "where my mother's house-keeper, Joyce, has so kindly arranged an impromptu reception for me and my new bride." The irony in his voice was barely discernible, but to Miranda it was patently obvious. Had this man really been jilted? She still could not reconcile herself to such an idea. The trio in the back seat lapsed into an expectant silence, giving Miranda the opportunity to assimilate everything that had happened since she had opened the door of this plush vehicle.

Clete turned his head to the window, his face expressionless as he stared out at the passing scenery. Miranda studied his stark profile outlined by the light of the afternoon sun high in the northern sky.

His black hair was slightly rumpled as if he had been running distracted fingers through its thickness. Miranda had an almost uncontrollable urge to raise her hands and smooth it for him. What was getting into her? She wondered with quick irritation. Admittedly it had been a long, grueling day, filled with strange emotions and events. Perhaps she was still in shock from this morning's revelations by her father and her fiancé—ex-fiancé, she corrected herself, or perhaps it was the lingering after effects of the wine she had consumed on the plane. Nonetheless her gaze was drawn and held by Clete Montana's magnetic figure.

At the same time he turned and looked down at Miranda and flashed a wide, charming smile that made her breath catch in her throat. She could not draw her eyes away from his.

"My friends and colleagues will be pleasantly surprised by the bride I present to them—if you have no objection, of course?" His voice was low so as not to disturb his mother.

"Do I have a choice?" Miranda inquired under her breath.

"Yes!" He looked surprised and raised one dark brow in serious question.

"Then we'll talk first, please, before we go in?" Why on earth was she contemplating going on with this wild masquerade? Miranda wondered. It was crazy to even think about it, she told herself. But on the other hand, these two had gotten her out of what could have been a sticky situation with Pace Dickinson. If her father learned where she was, he would ruthlessly hunt her down, she was sure of it. She owed these two people something for sparing her from that situation. And this man, Clete Montana

. . . she could definitely sympathize with him. They had, after all, something in common, both had apparently been deceived in love.

The car rolled to a smooth stop and the chauffeur stepped out and opened the door smartly on the old woman's side.

"You go on in, Mother," Clete told her, drawing Miranda even closer to his chest. "We'll follow in just a moment."

His mother laughed as she extended a hand to the waiting chauffeur. "Well, don't be too long, you lovebirds. Your guests are waiting and, after all, you have a lifetime of love ahead of you. Plenty of time for smooching later on!" She chuckled almost girlishly at her own words.

Adam helped Clete's mother out of the car and escorted her down a well-landscaped walkway. Miranda could hear their voices murmuring to one another as they turned a corner and disappeared behind an artistic grouping of birch trees. For the first time, Miranda noticed her surroundings and was pleasantly surprised. Acres of wooded land encompassed a log and stone house that spread out in several wings, the structure rambling and set amid lush green grass. In the distance, she detected the blue glint of water, probably an icy mountain lake. She heard a door open in the distance and the muted sounds of a party drifted out toward them. Then the door closed and once more the air was silent. Only the occasional chirping of a bird flying overhead disturbed the peaceful setting.

The man at her side sighed as he removed his left arm from around Miranda's shoulder. The action brought her attention back to the impending situation. Clete sat up straight as if to brace himself for battle as he turned to face her.

Piercing eyes of the warmest, deepest brown held her silvery gray ones captive. "Can I hope that you'll help me out of an extremely embarrassing situation?" It was time for Miranda to make a decision.

Chapter Two

Miranda lifted a slender hand to her temple. "I'm so confused," she murmured. "I . . . I was trying to get away from that man at the airport, and the only place to hide was this car."

"I thought it was something like that. A desperation, you might say, very much like the feeling I was facing before I opened the door of this car and found you." His expression was serious.

Miranda nodded her head. "And you were kind enough not to throw me out of the car immediately. Why, I could have been intent on doing someone harm! You would have had no way of knowing." Her hands gripped the bouquet of roses resting in her lap.

The man shook his dark head as he scrutinized her pale face. "Never. I could tell right away that you and I are kindred spirits." He spoke quietly, his deep, attractive voice exuding honesty. His manner instilled complete confidence in his listener. "It isn't just that man at the airport that brought you here, is it?" He was perceptive, too, Miranda realized as she lifted her eyes to his once more. She knew she could trust him with her story and she shook her head ruefully.

"This morning I discovered that the two men in my life were not at all what they appeared." Her wide gray eyes could not hide her shattered emotions from Clete's scrutiny.

"It seems we've both had our share of problems," he responded. "One short telephone call when I was out seems to have set a strange chain of events in motion." His words were brittle.

"And one short conversation that I wasn't supposed to overhear launched me into an adventure I never expected," Miranda countered, and their eyes met for a long, intense moment that she broke with a sigh.

"And here we are," Clete said, "our paths crossing through no planning of our own." His eyes raked over her features with a look that sent the blood rushing in her veins. His every glance had a strange effect on her senses. He took her hand in his once more.

"My mother, Elizabeth, and my housekeeper, Joyce, are so ecstatic over my change of marital status that they've arranged an impromptu reception. All my friends and relatives are eager to meet the woman who finally made me see the error of my bachelor ways." His voice held a teasing quality that was undeniably appealing.

"Will you bail me out then, and see this day through as Mrs. Clete Montana?" Clete smiled down at her beguilingly and again Miranda's heart skipped a beat.

"It's the least I can do, isn't it . . . Clete?" She savored the sound of his name on her lips and, not daring to lift her eyes, she fastened her gaze on her hand held in his.

"You're an angel of mercy!" he exclaimed, pulling her to him in a spontaneous hug that left her breathless as she inhaled the heady masculine scent of his aftershave lotion. Her soft cheek was rubbed against his firm one before he released her from the unexpected and enthusiastic embrace. She heard him laugh softly. "I don't even know your name!" he said.

"Mir . . . Mandy," she stammered. It was the pet name her mother had always used. The name had a special connotation for her, and it somehow seemed appropriate at this moment.

"Mandy," Clete murmured. "Come on then, Mandy, our guests are waiting," he said, his tone wry once more.

He opened the door on his side of the limousine and slid out, drawing Miranda gently with him. As she stood up, clutching the bouquet of roses, she felt even more overwhelmed by his towering figure. His shoulders looked wider, his arms and legs more powerful than before. His suit fit him to perfection, she realized as he straightened his tie. He wore a vest that matched the jacket and slacks, the material a nubby dark beige highlighted by subtle white pin stripes. The suit was cut in the European style, and the effect was dashing yet masculine, his white silk shirt contrasting sharply with his golden tan. As close to him as Mandy was, she could make out the minute geometric Indian design of gold that slanted across his brown tie.

Suddenly she became aware of how she must appear, her long hair streaming over her shoulders, her lipstick surely a thing of the past!

"Oh, I must look a sight! At least let me put on my jacket and freshen my makeup." Clete took the bouquet from her arms and with a free hand deftly assisted her with her white jacket, which was unwrinkled due to the modern miracle fabric. She fumbled in her purse and drew out a pair of tortoiseshell combs, intending to pin her hair neatly away from her face.

"Let me help," Clete offered. He laid the bridal bouquet on the vinyl roof of the limousine, first breaking off a cluster of white baby's breath. He took the combs out of her suddenly clumsy fingers and attached the lacy flowers to one of the decorative combs. Gently he caught a swath of her thick brown tresses and secured it behind one shell-shaped ear, pushing the long length back over her shoulder. Before Mandy knew his intention, he arranged her hair to drape forward over the other shoulder. Thick waves rested seductively against her cheek.

"Perfect," Clete pronounced. He slipped the extra comb into the pocket of his suit jacket.

Disconcerted by his close attention, Miranda nervously dropped her fingers to the unbuttoned vee of her blouse that showed too much of her creamy skin for her own peace of mind. But Clete's warm fingers met hers, his hands brushing intimately against her breast. "This looks fine just the way it is,

Mandy," he chided softly as his eyes feasted upon the creamy swell beneath his fingers. At his light touch, a shock of awareness rushed through Miranda's body, her nerve ends tingling fiercely. It was as if all her extremities had been without circulation for a long time and had just now been awakened. She felt as if she burned at his every touch. Flustered, she stepped back to a safe distance and fumbled in her handbag for her lipstick. Once more he stopped her with a firm hand.

"My lipstick . . ." Her voice trailed off as a decisive hand moved to grasp her chin and tilted her face inexorably upward. He bent his own dark head to meet hers halfway and kissed her full on the mouth. The kiss lasted only an instant, yet it was unbelievably thorough if her rocketing pulse and weakening legs were any indication.

"There," Clete murmured with satisfaction, "now you look like a bride is supposed to look. Beautifully flushed and well-kissed!" His eyes glittered as their gazes met and held for an electric moment. She tried to tell herself that he had an ulterior motive for kissing her and that it didn't mean a thing. Yet she felt as if her bones had turned to honey and were slowly melting away in the sweetness that permeated her very core. From somewhere far away, a thought floated into her befuddled mind, a realization that no other man had ever brought the same kind of havoc to her senses. She couldn't remember when she had experienced such an urgent need to reciprocate a man's embrace as she did at this moment. But Clete was handing her the bouquet of white roses. His hand was at her waist as he guided Miranda up the stone walkway. They moved past the copse of delicate birch trees to the entrance of the impressive house, the portico decorated with a welcoming profusion of colorful trailing flowers in hanging baskets.

She was brought out of the daze the kiss had inflicted on her as Clete lifted her unexpectedly into his strong arms and carried her over the threshold of his home. Inside the warm, inviting entryway, Miranda could hear the sounds of a party. As Clete set her down gently, his hands slipped up to her shoulders and he smiled tenderly down at her.

"We have to make this look authentic," he murmured and made a move to draw her closer, his words reminding her that this was not real, that it was all a crazy masquerade on their part to save Clete and, in particular his mother, embarrassment. He was merely acting out his part as a happy bridegroom! Yet her heart beat an erratic tune at his touch, at his every move. Then the "newlyweds" became the center of attention and the warm gaze of Miranda's make-believe bridegroom was turned on his family and friends.

"Here are the bride and groom!" "Welcome home!" Good wishes flowed forth as Clete and Mandy were drawn into a large living area crowded with guests. The spacious, airy room was tastefully decorated, yet it exuded a warmth that made a visitor forget the obvious value of the well-chosen antiques. Mandy began to relax despite the unusual circumstances of her presence. She even felt at home with Clete Montana whom she had known scarcely more than an hour. Yet standing across the room from him sometime later, she realized he represented a form of comfort she had never before experienced. She knew that if she needed him he would come to her without question. Of course, it was important that he appear like a captivated bridegroom if they were to be successful with their masquerade. But Mandy knew he was a man to be depended upon despite the winding road of deceit on which they had embarked. Why she felt this way about a perfect stranger, she could not fathom. Yet as she watched him conversing with a group of his close business associates across the room, she was certain of her analysis.

"I hope you are enjoying the reception?" Joyce inquired.

"Everything is lovely," Mandy reassured the housekeeper. They stood side by side glancing about the festive room. Guests were being served champagne punch by a friendly woman whose name Miranda could not remember, but she recalled that the woman had been introduced as a neighbor and close friend of the Montana family.

"You did a marvelous job and on such short notice, too," Mandy complimented Joyce after a comfortable silence.

"Yes, well, it was just a matter of getting the flowers and cake to the house. This place is so big, and Clete's been so busy with work that the only rooms used lately are his bedroom and bathroom."

"But I assumed Mrs. Mon . . . Elizabeth lived here with Clete."

"Good heavens, no! Oh, she and I spend some holidays here, and Elizabeth helped Clete a great deal by decorating this place, but we live in a penthouse apartment in Anchorage. Elizabeth finds it more convenient to be in the city, close to the museums and theaters, where things are happening, so to speak. And I manage Clete's housekeeping, but that's more of an organizing job than work. When you return from your honeymoon, I'll give you the list of outside help that I use here, plus an outline of all the other services available. Then you and Clete will be on your own and I'll be even closer to retirement." Joyce smiled warmly at Mandy, who remained silent. She was learning so much about Clete and his life-style.

Earlier he had introduced her to various business-men that worked for Montana-Hudson Mining, the company Clete owned and ran. Apparently, he was an excellent mining engineer, as was his father before him. Clete seemed to be as liked and respect-ed as the late Andrew Montana had been, from whom Clete had inherited the company. The Montana family had lived in Alaska since the famous gold rush in 1898.

Slowly a picture of the person called Clete Montana was beginning to form in her mind. He had a way with people, she could personally testify to that, and he had a way with youngsters, too. She had seen the rapport that existed between him and the three children at the reception, the two girls and the boy whose mother was serving the punch. Clete had not ignored the youngsters, as so many men arriving at a reception in their honor might have done. He had made a point to speak to all three and had personally introduced each to Mandy, speaking to them in the same tone of voice he used to introduce his adult guests. No wonder they loved Clete, and the feeling was mutual, she could see. Her gaze was once more drawn to his tall figure across the wide room.

To her surprise, she found Clete watching her and she flushed. Why was she letting his glances disconcert her like this? she wondered angrily. She had never been given to childish blushes, and she had successfully existed in a predominantly male world for many years now. She was afraid he could read her increasingly intimate thoughts centered around . . . around him.

Clete walked across the room toward Mandy to join her and the housekeeper. "I've come to claim my bride, Joyce." Joyce moved quickly away, although Mandy scarcely noticed her departure. "It's time to cut the cake." His firm hand at the small of her back guided Miranda to the dining room table. Their guests, alerted that something propitious was about to commence, crowded around the "bride and groom."

Joyce reappeared carrying a small but beautifully decorated three-tier wedding cake. She set it on the dining room table to the sound of enthusiastic applause. Miranda was seized by an intense feeling of nervousness. Clete squeezed Mandy's hand reassuringly. Not giving her time to dwell on the situation, he picked up a silver cake knife decorated with a white silk bow. With a wide, engaging smile, he drew Miranda securely into the circle of his arms and put the knife into her trembling hand, covering it with his larger one and guiding her through the ritual of cutting the wedding cake.

The "groom" helped his "bride" to the first piece of cake. Someone handed Mandy a fork and turning inside the confines of Clete's embrace, she instinctively played out her own role.

With a slight tremble, she lifted a piece of cake on

the fork, moving it upward to Clete's mouth. He grinned as he accepted her offering, and then, amid enthusiastic applause, he took the fork from her hand and reciprocated. As she took a delicate bite of the delicious cake, her eyes met his in a long, unbroken glance that intensified as he bent and moved closer, the smile on his attractive face fading as his lips brushed the corner of her mouth. She felt his tongue caress her lower lip as he removed a minute trace of the fluffy icing from her tender skin. "Ummm, delicious . . ." he murmured and his breath mingled sweetly with Miranda's.

They were interrupted by teasing calls to share the cake. Clete smiled as he drew away from Miranda. She moved her tongue unconsciously over the place where his had lingered, savoring the taste of sweetness left behind. Miranda turned and by chance caught Elizabeth Montana's all-seeing gaze full upon her. Clete's mother looked at Miranda, her old eyes serious but warm with understanding. She nodded her head ever so slightly, as if to tell the younger girl she understood fully and gave Mandy her blessing. What a wonderful mother-in-law she would make someone, Miranda thought, saddened by the idea of Elizabeth ultimately discovering the truth behind this "wedding" party.

The neighbor who was serving punch moved to help cut and serve the cake to the guests. Miranda heard Clete thanking her, calling her Jane. Jane's husband, Todd Kelly, materialized at Mandy's side with the three children in tow.

"Mandy, I know today has been very confusing for you—I don't think you expected all this, did you?"

That was an understatement if she'd ever heard one! Mandy shook her head and smiled politely, if somewhat wearily.

"We'll get to know you better after your honeymoon," Todd reassured her. He sent his children off to get some cake from their mother. "I must say, everyone here is pleasantly surprised with Clete's choice. I knew he had good taste in women, but he's outdone himself this time!"

"I heard that, Todd, and I fully concur." Clete was at Miranda's side once more. He was playing the perfect bridegroom. Miranda noted and was shocked to feel a sharp stab of something amazingly similar to jealousy. Jealousy of what? she wondered as Todd and Clete talked and joked easily with one another. After all, she was on the receiving end of all his masculine attention right now. It didn't make sense to her tired mind.

"Mandy, dear child, why don't you come with me to freshen up? You look almost done in." Elizabeth was at her side.

"Good idea. It's almost time to leave," Clete said. Miranda's pulse quickened. Leave? Where? She looked at Clete in askance but he had already turned to talk to Todd again. Elizabeth took Mandy's arm and guided her down a wide corridor to another wing of the house. The charade was almost over, Miranda realized. All it had been was a brief interlude in her life. She felt sad at the thought.

It was almost shocking to remember she had known the Montanas for only a few hours.

Elizabeth led Miranda into a large room decorated in rust and jade green. In the center, a king-sized brass bed caught her eye immediately, its massive expanse covered by a quilted jade-colored spread, the rich damask fabric decorated with rust and jade peacocks nestling in brown and beige reeds.

"This is Clete's room," his mother told her, "and yours now, too, Mandy." She motioned toward the bathroom. "I'll wait here while you freshen up, my dear." Elizabeth settled herself slowly at the edge of the large bed.

Mandy hurriedly refreshed her makeup, this time adding the lipstick she had desired earlier. Her thoughts went back to the moment Clete had kissed her. It had seemed so natural, so right, nothing at all like when Dayton had kissed her. Miranda could not meet her own eyes in the mirror at the thought and she quickly washed her hands, patting her color-heightened cheeks with cool water. Stepping out of the bathroom, she noticed how pale Elizabeth appeared. This had been too much excitement for the old lady, Miranda realized anxiously. She did not look well at all.

Hearing Mandy's footsteps, Elizabeth sat up straighter and fixed a smile on her lined face. Miranda felt a rush of affection for the woman who so obviously loved her son and had only his happiness in mind.

"You're not well, are you?" Miranda said quietly and looked the woman straight in the eye. As before, they seemed to understand one another, and Elizabeth shook her head.

"But I don't want Clete to know! He deserves some time alone with you, he's worked so hard since his father died two years ago!" A sad look crossed her face. "I was beginning to think my son would never slow down, never settle down to the happiness he deserves! My time is limited and I did so hope to see my grandchildren before I left." A tender smile touched the old lady's lips. "Now I have some hope that will help me hang on a bit longer."

"Oh, please!" Miranda became distressed, not only at the sad tone, but at the thought that she was doing the woman a disservice by deceiving her. "You have a lot of time yet. You just have to take good care of yourself!" Miranda stood in front of Elizabeth, daring to take one of the old hands in hers. Somehow she felt very protective of Clete's mother.

Elizabeth stood up and gave Mandy an impulsive hug. "With you here to help me, to love Clete the way he needs, I think I could last longer than I had hoped!"

Embracing the woman tightly, Miranda closed her eyes as tears threatened. This woman deserved so much more than she was getting! The deceit she and Clete were engaged in clutched at her heart. She finally opened her eyes to find Clete watching them. He looked pensive, his expression serious for a long moment as he and Miranda stared at one another. Then he seemed to pull himself together and entered his bedroom.

"Are you ready to go, Mandy?" The time had come to say good-bye to these people she had only just met. She nodded, not trusting herself to speak.

Clete ushered Miranda and Elizabeth down the hallway and back into the living room. He gave his mother one last piercing look and hugged her quickly and tightly. Mandy kissed the age-softened cheeks and let Clete guide her away.

He did not take her out the front door as she had expected. Instead he led her through a set of French doors onto a wooden deck outside. The sun was sinking in the west. The northern air had a crisp feel to it, especially when they moved through patches of shade beneath the aspens and birches. Lights danced off the rippling waves of the lake as the evening breeze shifted slightly. The guests followed closely behind.

"Thank you, everyone!" Clete called and turned to wave. Mandy followed suit.

"Where to now?" she murmured as Clete wrapped an arm around her slender waist and guided her down a steep set of wooden steps. The heavily wooded lot slanted sharply downward to the moss-covered shore.

"Now we fade slowly into the sunset," he quipped as he flashed her a wide grin. The wedding party had congregated on the deck above them to shower the "bride and groom" with grains of rice. Mandy gave a squeal of surprise, and Clete laughed down at her, delight written over his handsome features.

Grabbing her hand, he broke into a run and pulled Mandy across a boardwalk of wooden slats that led to the lake's edge where it narrowed into a wooden dock projecting out over the water. At the end of the dock a small sleek airplane rested, floating on pontoons. Clete helped her carefully but quickly through the door, the craft dipping and swaying beneath her like a boat. She noticed that her suitcase was stowed neatly beside one of rich dark leather that she assumed belonged to Clete. Beside their two cases were several bulging duffel bags and various cardboard boxes.

Clete assisted Miranda with her seat belt and, with thorough and efficient movements, he soon had the engine purring to life, the propellers becoming invisible as they increased speed and caught. With a last wave at friends and relatives on the deck, Clete guided the floatplane out onto open water and positioned it for takeoff. Miranda had never been in this type of craft before. She paid close attention to Clete's every movement as he concentrated on the liftoff. The water around them became a blur of gray blue as the pontoons left the lake behind. From their increasingly lofty height, she could see the magnificent homes nestled in the thickly wooded forest surrounding the indigo lake. Several more floatplanes were berthed at various docks.

Clete curved the small plane in a wide arc and flew back toward the house. He dropped altitude slightly and dipped the wings from side to side in a playful sign of recognition. The guests on the deck waved and then the plane shot over the house. Miranda's pulse quickened as Clete flashed her a wide grin, and then pulled back on the stick, causing the small craft to climb sharply. Finally he leveled off at a cruising altitude and glanced over at his passenger once again.

"Where can I drop you?" The question, in light of their location, caught Miranda off guard. Her eyes widened and she burst into delighted laughter. After a second, Clete realized what he had just said and joined in with her merriment, a much needed relief from the strain of the deception they had just undergone.

"Don't take that literally, please!"

"I'm sorry, I knew what you meant, really!" Miranda replied after catching her breath. She shook her head slowly and shrugged. "It doesn't matter where I go, I didn't have an itinerary."

Something in her tone of voice must have alerted him for he shot her a piercing look. "Won't someone be wondering where you are?"

She thought seriously about his question. George or Dayton wouldn't have received her postcards yet. They would most likely assume that she was still at the drill site. "No," she replied slowly, "there's no one to worry about me at all."

If Clete was puzzled, he tactfully refrained from comment. "I want to thank you for doing what you did—I realize you're not a person to take such deception lightly, but under the circumstances I feel my actions this afternoon were justified."

"Justified?" she questioned, her voice low and soft as if she were mulling over the meaning of the word. "It was a cruel thing to do."

Her words surprised him, his eyebrow shooting upward in question. "We made a lot of people happy today," he countered.

"Today, perhaps, but how is your mother going to react when she learns the truth?"

"She's not going to find out."

"And how will you manage that?" Miranda shot back.

"I'll just tell her the marriage was a mistake and we separated." He had every angle figured out.

"And you don't think that's cruel? Why, she's already talking of grandchildren in the near future!"

Clete sighed, the sound coming from deep within his chest. "I know," he agreed. "This is what's called being caught between a rock and a hard place." Now it was Miranda's time to raise an eyebrow in question. "My mother has been ill for quite some time now. She doesn't think I realize how serious it is; it's her heart and, under the circumstances, I was concerned about making an appearance without the expected bride." His voice was dry with irony and a strange kind of anger. "Mother knew Fern and I had known one another years ago. When Fern answered the phone in my hotel room, she apparently told Elizabeth we were on our way to our wedding." He told Miranda this in a tightly controlled voice, and she didn't have to ask who Fern was. "When Adam met me inside the terminal and told me about the impromptu reception, I started to worry . . . but there you were," he continued, his mood changing. "Almost a gift from heaven!" he pronounced. Across the small space of the cockpit, they shared a smile at the bizarre twist of fate that had brought them to this point.

"So you took a chance on a complete stranger, just to spare Elizabeth the embarrassment of having to explain her son's situation to a houseful of wedding guests," Mandy summarized.

"Well, I think my gamble paid off—you were a smash hit!" For all the good it had done her, Miranda thought with a strange sense of despondency. Clete continued. "I really do appreciate your bailing me out."

"If I helped any at all, then I'm glad," she responded stiffly, slightly embarrassed.

"You know, you're a very nice person."

For a moment, Miranda stared at his strong profile. He was so much in control, his long lean fingers depicting a sense of power where they rested on the controls. Her heart fluttered strangely as she took in the meaning of his kindly spoken words. She did not know if she liked his observation or not. It was not exactly the feeling she wanted him to have for her. They both lapsed into a thoughtful silence, the only sound the smooth drone of the engine.

"Where are we going?" she inquired finally as her eyes skimmed the dark green of endless forest beneath them. The shadow of the plane sped ahead of them, a dark, clinging shape that molded itself to the contours of the wilderness spreading out below the craft.

"Well, I had always planned that when I married, my wife and I would honeymoon at my cabin in the Talkeetna Mountains." His voice sounded suddenly stiff, and Miranda wondered if there was more to the story than he was telling her. Had he and Fern really been on the brink of marriage as Elizabeth had been led to understand? She sympathized with him if that was really the case. She knew firsthand the disillusionment of such a situation. Her eyes strayed to his wide-shouldered figure sitting so close to her and, covertly, she studied everything about him, enjoying the sight of him. His dark hair was thick and wavy, his profile was strong, his nose straight and well shaped, his mouth firm, decisive. He was more than just handsome. His entire being gave the impression of strength and intelligence. Her eyes continued down the length of his well-muscled shoulders and chest, his tapered waist, his long legs. Suddenly she was swamped with relief that he hadn't married the lady called Fern. Guiltily, she looked away from him.

"Right now, I'm headed for a fishing trip at my cabin," Clete explained, finishing the answer to her question as his mouth slanted sideways in a wry smile. Miranda could not meet his intent brown eyes.

"Can you arrange transportation for me when we arrive? A plane or even a bus would be fine."

"You really don't have anywhere specific you have to go?" He shot her another sharp glance before returning his attention to the instrument panel.

"No," she answered slowly, "nowhere at all." Fleetingly she realized she should not be admitting such a thing to a strange man, but Clete was special somehow. She trusted him implicitly and had no qualms that he would take advantage of her lonely state. She was not afraid of him.

"Well, then, how does a genuine Alaskan vacation in the bush sound?"

Miranda jerked her head toward Clete in surprise, her heart stopping for a long moment. "What are you suggesting?" she demanded, trying desperately to conceal her sudden breathlessness.

"I feel that you and I could be good friends, Mandy. I owe you a real debt of gratitude. . . ." She shook her head and made as if to interrupt. "No, no, let me finish. I feel very comfortable with you, almost as if we've known one another for a long time." She felt the same way, but refrained from giving an answer.

"I have two bedrooms at my cabin; it's quiet, peaceful in a very special way. Out there you can commune with nature, think things out clearly with no outside pressure . . ." His voice trailed off as he reverted to thought. Caught up in the same mood, Mandy also let her mind wander for a long moment.

"It sounds heavenly," she finally admitted.

"Then you'll come with me? It's remote, virtually isolated in the wilderness—no planes or buses to escape on—and you'll have to share the chores with me!" he warned her with pseudo-gruffness, his grin lopsided and boyish, the light in his eyes turning them to amber gold.

"If you put it that way . . ." Mandy drawled softly, throwing him a quick glance, "I accept!" She was becoming accustomed to making spot decisions, and strangely the thought made her giggle. Perhaps she had taken too much champagne punch.

Chapter Three

It was late in the evening when the small floatplane circled and dipped down to let the pontoons skim and meld with the dark surface of a wilderness lake. This far north there were almost twenty hours of daylight and the sun had just barely disappeared behind the mountain peaks to the west. The dense forest of evergreen was like a thick dark blanket over the earth as far as the eye could see. When the craft came to a stop at the weathered dock sticking out into the pewter-sheened lake and the engine was cut off, the silence of the surrounding mountains and woods settled about Clete and Mandy. They disembarked and walked without speaking across the planks of the dock; the sound of their footsteps seemed an intrusion in the serenity of the scene. Side by side on the grassy shore they looked toward the welcoming cabin nestled in a copse of protecting

evergreen trees. The air was cold and Miranda felt
its sharpness penetrate her lightweight jacket. She
shivered slightly.

Clete was immediately contrite. "You're freez-
ing!" He took her firmly by the arm and led her up a
path, which was cleared neatly of rocks and stumps.
"Let me check out the cabin first," he insisted as he
slipped out of his beige suit jacket and slid it over
Miranda's shoulders. The warmth from his body and
the scent of his cologne enveloped her, pleasantly
assailing her tired senses. He did not seem to mind
the chill in the air. "I don't want to startle a wary
animal that might have burrowed in during my
absence."

Miranda's curiosity was piqued. She looked
around with interest. "What kind of creatures are we
apt to find?" she asked, a smile curving her soft lips.
Clete's gaze fastened on her mouth for a moment
before answering with a smile.

"One year we had to evict a family of skunks!"

"Heavens, that could have terrible side effects."
Miranda laughed.

"Let's just say we slept under the stars for longer
than we liked!" Clete's deep chuckle reverberated
through the cabin as he stepped cautiously inside.

Mandy waited patiently at the door and hugged
his jacket tightly to her as she studied the rustic
structure in the dying light. The walls were made of
logs stripped of bark, the cracks chinked with bright
green moss. On either side of the planked door was a
small multi-paned window of clear glass. Tall grass
grew thickly around the foundation. It looked as if it
had been a very long time since anyone had stayed
here. Glancing upward, she could see that the cabin
had a sod roof, a combination of moss, grasses and

wildflowers growing in thick harmony over wooden planking. In the darkening shadows of the night, Miranda felt as if she and Clete had stepped into the past and were the only two people in the world. There was not a light to be seen anywhere and the quickly stealing night was thick with primitive shapes. What a distance she had covered since early that morning, she thought with wonder as her eyes swept over the spectacular scene. She shook her head slightly.

Miranda heard Clete call her name. She turned and entered the cabin slowly. "Is it safe?" she called softly. Clete had lit several candles and an old-fashioned kerosene lamp. The room had the warm glow of hospitality.

"All clear," he answered from across the room. "No skunks in sight, but don't get frightened if you see an occasional ball of fur scurrying from corner to corner. It'll just be a harmless shrew or an inquisitive field mouse."

"As long as there are no snakes, I'll be all right," Mandy replied, fully aware that he expected the typical female reaction at the mention of a rodent. Clete busied himself by starting a fire in an old-fashioned wood stove with a flat top that provided a cooking surface.

"No snakes in Alaska," Clete reassured her, "just bear, moose, caribou, wolves . . . I could go on, but I don't want to scare you off on your first night here!" His teeth flashed white as he slanted her a smile.

Mandy stepped closer to the stove, the flame inside already radiating a small amount of comforting warmth. "You can't scare me. I'm from Texas. Anything you have here, we have bigger," she teased, matching his smile with a tired grin, "not to mention we have more than our share of scorpions, rattlesnakes and tarantulas. And I've camped out with the best of them, I can assure you!"

Clete stood up, dusting his hands together to rid them of ashes and wood shavings. His eyes reflected the dim light as they roamed over her, the designer suit and shoes incongruous in the rustic surroundings. "You somehow don't look the type to enjoy camping," he remarked.

Disconcerted by his masculine scrutiny, Miranda defended herself. "Well, I don't normally dress like this in the middle of the woods. I assure you I've done my share of campground cooking and sleeping under the open skies. I've even shot a rattlesnake or two!" she added with a certain amount of relish, lifting her chin in defiance.

Clete laughed out loud. "You're full of surprises, Mandy! I really am looking forward to getting to know all about the rough and tough side of you!" His brown eyes mirrored the gold of the flames visible in the opening in the wood stove. "But right now, I'd better get our gear so you can get out of those fancy clothes. You won't be needing them for a while!"

So he had noticed the quality of her garments, Mandy thought as she watched him stride out of the cabin, his shoulder muscles drawing the material of his shirt taut. He was a man who would be very observant of women and what they wore, and Mandy could not banish the idea that he would be even more observant of what they did not wear. She blushed at the intimate thought, remembering suddenly that this could have been his honeymoon hideaway. She stepped to the door of the cabin and peered out into the shadows. Holding her arm up to catch the light from the lamp, she checked the time. Her watch read 5:00 A.M., she saw with a shock. Then she remembered it was still set to Houston time. That made the actual time one o'clock in the morning, and the sun had just barely set! No wonder she was tired. In fact, she realized as she slumped against the door frame, she was exhausted. Her head rested against the rough wood as she tried desperately to keep her eyelids open.

With a start, Mandy stood straight up. Clete had touched her wrist and was pulling her toward him. With an arm around her shoulders, which was still covered with his suit jacket, he led her into the nearest bedroom. She wondered how long she had been standing asleep in the doorway. She noted sleepily that he had already carried in her small case. On a bedside table, a candle wavered in the air currents created as Clete and Mandy moved around the room.

"You get out your nightgear while I make the bed," Clete ordered. Mandy nodded, strangely affected by the sight of the tall, competent man taking charge, pulling out clean bed linen that was stored neatly away in airtight bags. She turned to rummage around in her suitcase to find the only item suitable for sleeping. It was a black negligee she had thrown in. Of course at the time she had packed it, she had never imagined she would end up in the remote Alaskan wilderness. It was too lightweight to be of any use here! She voiced the thought out loud without even thinking as she turned to face Clete, the nightgown held in front of her graphic demonstration. Her smile faded as she saw his smoldering eyes.

"Yes, it's certainly suited to a more fitting occasion, isn't it? Like a honeymoon," he said, his voice rasping in his throat. Mutely, Mandy wondered whose ill-fated honeymoon he was thinking of, hers with her greedy fiancé, or his with the woman he had left behind in Las Vegas? They stared across the room at one another for a timeless moment.

Then Clete moved toward her with firm, measured steps. "Let's put this away, Mandy," he said. "I'll get you a pair of my mother's thermal underwear. They double as a great pair of pajamas." After folding the black nightgown quickly and returning it to her suitcase, Clete strode to a wall of shelves. In another airtight bag, he found the thermal clothing and handed them to Mandy, who was waiting patiently but wearily beside the bed.

"Do you need anything else?" he asked, towering over her slight form. She could not see his expression in the flickering candlelight that cast his wavering shadow over her.

Miranda shook her head mutely. Clete bent and cupped her face with his strong hands. Then he brushed his lips across her forehead in a featherlight touch. As Mandy lifted her face to stare up at him with slumberous eyes, Clete pushed her long hair away from her shoulders where the tresses had been caught by his jacket.

"Thank you again, Mandy, for everything you've done today." He turned away, closing the bedroom door quietly, leaving Miranda alone to settle herself in bed.

Miranda stretched her limbs like a lazy cat, the down quilt warming her with its soft comfort. She felt completely rested from her night of sleep, but as she opened her eyes to the dimness of the room, she experienced a moment of confusion. It was not the room her brain was expecting to see first thing in the morning. Then she turned toward the closed door and remembered.

She bounded out of bed with a burst of energy, but the chill air reminded her immediately that she was not dressed properly. Quickly she dug around in her suitcase, then tugged on form-fitting blue denim jeans and the only long-sleeved blouse she had packed. She brushed her long hair until the mink brown strands crackled with static. The only other pair of shoes she had besides the elegant snakeskin sandals were her tennis shoes, so they would have to suffice. Carefully, she opened the door to her bedroom and peeked out into the great room that served as kitchen, dining room, and living area in the cabin. Clete was nowhere to be seen.

Mandy pulled the door to the bedroom closed behind her for she felt the warmth of the fire in the stove and did not want it to escape the living area. Sniffing the air appreciatively, she caught the welcomed aroma of fresh coffee and spied an old-fashioned metal pot warming on the back burner of the stove. Clean mugs were stored on a set of shelves behind a rectangular table of rough wood planking. She helped herself to the coffee. Wondering where Clete was, she was about to knock on the closed door of his bedroom when the front door opened. Clete stepped in carrying an aluminum pan filled with freshly cleaned lake trout.

"Good morning, sleepyhead." He grinned at her while his masculine gaze assessed her slender figure in jeans and sports shirt with open approval. He acted as if they had shared a cabin many times before.

"I just now got up and was wondering where you were." She smiled, feeling shy despite his casual attitude.

"How did you sleep?"

"I've never slept better," Mandy admitted. "It must be all this fresh air."

Clete nodded his dark head. "I hope it's doing something for your appetite because there's enough here to feed an army!"

"You've been busy," she said, admiring the fresh fish. "You must have been up since the crack of dawn."

"Practically," Clete admitted. "Breakfast is coming right up. You just sit down and get comfortable."

"But can't I help?" Miranda offered. "The deal was for me to share the chores."

"If it makes you feel better, you can clean up," Clete told her with a boyish grin. "I hate doing dishes."

"Oh, so you have an ulterior motive!" Mandy settled herself on one of the ladder-backed wooden chairs at the kitchen table, one slender leg tucked beneath her. She sipped her coffee as she watched him fixing the first meal of the day.

"To be fair, I guess we can alternate," Clete responded to her last comment. "Today, I cook, you clean. Tomorrow, you cook, and I clean. Fair enough?" He shot a quick glance her way, one eyebrow lifted quizzically.

"Perfectly," Mandy agreed, satisfied with the proposal.

Clete expertly salted and floured the fish and

arranged them neatly in a large black iron skillet. As they fried, he produced a packet of dried eggs, mixing in bottled water from a plastic container in preparation for cooking. All the while he punctuated his lithe movements with occasional comments. It pleased Mandy that he did not seem compelled to entertain her with mere chitchat. Instead he explained to her that he had a gasoline-operated generator that he used to power the pump on the water well his grandfather had installed. The cabin sported indoor plumbing complete with an old-fashioned tank toilet and a claw-footed bathtub. At this point he warned her never to drink the water from a lake or stream without boiling or treating it with chemicals first. He elaborated on the organisms in Alaskan waters that were highly dangerous and, at the least, could make one very ill. His well water had been tested and found safe for drinking. He showed her where all the cooking utensils and food supplies were located as he moved about the kitchen area. "Just so you won't have any excuse not to cook when your turn comes," he teased, winking at her.

Soon they were eating fried trout accompanied by scrambled eggs and sliced French bread that he had found packed in one of the boxes from the plane. "Adam really outdid himself when he packed the supplies. There's even wine and caviar."

"Nothing could top this meal, Clete." Mandy consumed the last bite of trout with unconcealed relish and leaned back in her chair with a deep sigh of contentment.

"I'm glad to see you're not one of those women who is constantly fussing over her figure. I'm sick to death of females who refuse to enjoy a meal or deny themselves the pleasure of having children just because it might put a few pounds on their sticklike shapes!" He spoke scornfully.

Mandy looked at him ruefully. "I love to eat," she admitted, "and so far I've never had a problem with weight." She sipped her third cup of coffee. "And I want a big family when Day and I get marr . . ." Her voice faltered and she stared at Clete with wide eyes. "I forgot for a minute, didn't I?" She set her cup down with leaden fingers and sighed. "Day insisted he didn't want children, but I never really believed him."

Clete reached across the table and took one of her slender hands in his, its masculine strength imparting comfort through the light touch.

"That sounds like Fern," he told her as he caressed the soft skin of Miranda's hand. "She wanted all the advantages of marriage with none of the responsibilities. Having children would ruin her figure, or so she said, and would take too much time away from her career."

"Your mother mentioned you had known her years ago," Miranda commented hesitantly, feeling an intense need to know more about Clete and his relationship with Fern.

Clete nodded at her statement. "That was before I inherited Montana-Hudson Mining from my father. I had been working as an engineer for my dad's company, and on the way home after a business trip, I stopped in Las Vegas with a group of friends. I'd been working too hard and needed a break before resuming work." By the faraway look in his eyes, Miranda could tell that his thoughts were in the distant past. "Fern was with a dancing troupe performing at one of the nightclubs. One of the guys knew another girl in the group, and she brought Fern

along after their performance. After that we started
to date. Fern didn't seem at all like the typical
showgirl type, and from almost the instant we
met, she and I spent every available minute together. . . ." Instinctively Miranda knew he and
Fern had had a more complicated relationship than
the word "dating" implied, and an undefinable
feeling swept through her at the thought. "But we
were young and it came to nothing. At the time she
was obsessed with becoming a successful dancer and
actress." Clete's voice trailed off for a reflective
moment.

"And then after all those years, we met again last
month in Las Vegas where it had all started," he
continued. "We caught up on everything that had
happened to one another over the years, her acting
career, my company. She made no secret of wanting to resume our relationship. One thing led to
another. . . ." Preoccupied with his thoughts, Clete
jumped up from the table, taking his mug with him
to refill it with hot coffee at the stove. Miranda could
not see his expression.

"But you know the conclusion of my story," he
said as he turned around and came back to the table.
With a scrape of the chair, Clete sat down opposite
Miranda once more. "What about you?" he questioned softly. She realized he wasn't going to tell her
anything else about his relationship with the mysteri-
ous woman called Fern.

Clete made it plain that it was Miranda's turn to
explain about her and Dayton Green. "I overheard
him and my father discussing the previous night out
on the town together—with their respective mis-
tresses." She ran a distracted hand through her loose
hair and pushed its thickness away from her pale

face. "I'm not such an innocent that I can't understand men like my father and Dayton needing feminine companionship from time to time, but Dayton and I had a commitment to one another! Then I heard them openly discussing the stocks in my father's company that Dayton would receive when we married. It was so cold, so calculating, Clete!" she cried, her voice intense with feeling. "I felt like a piece of livestock being sold on the block. The worst part about it all was that my mother had warned me over seven years ago—just before I last saw her, but I thought I knew better than she!"

"Is she . . . dead?" Clete asked quietly.

"No." Mandy shook her head sadly. "My parents separated and I stayed with my father. That was another thing I hadn't known about until yesterday. My dear father has something he's holding over my mother as a threat, and if she ever tries to see me he'll use the information to ruin Mother's second husband. All those years I thought she didn't want anything to do with me! My father even encouraged that belief, knowing full well how much my mother's indifference had hurt me. But yesterday morning I heard him and Day openly discussing me and my mother, not to mention all the other things." Her low voice sounded strained as she remembered all the unexpectedly cruel things she had overheard.

"So you ran away," Clete observed as he watched her face closely.

"It sounds so childish when you put it like that, but I knew exactly what I was doing," she answered seriously. "I realized that between the two of them, my father and Day had my entire life organized to suit themselves." Disgust at herself filled her voice.

"I never want to see my father or my fiancé . . . ex-fiancé, again!"

"And how did they react when you told them that?"

Miranda hesitated for a mere instant. "I didn't wait around for that. I wanted to do things my own way, shape my own destiny so to speak." Clete gave her a smile of indulgent skepticism, and Mandy realized he thought she was overreacting. She needed desperately to make him understand. "My father is a very powerful man, Clete," she explained, "and he'd find a way to stop me, that's for sure!" Now it was her turn to move away from the table. "I sent them a card to let them know that nothing had happened to me, but I didn't tell them where I was going." She carried their dishes to the sink set in a small alcove to one side of the room. "Not that I knew or even cared where I was going," she muttered with chagrin.

"What about the man you were running away from at the airport?" Clete followed her with his empty coffee cup. They faced one another in front of the window over the sink, and she saw the look in his brown eyes. He still thought she was exaggerating, she thought.

"He's an executive at one of my father's branch offices in Dallas, and I just didn't want my whereabouts to get back to the all-powerful George Bridger!" Miranda defended herself in a vehement voice, revealing her father's identity.

The impact on Clete was startling, his lean, powerfully built body going taut with surprise. He took a backward step. Obviously, Miranda thought, he had heard of the influential oil magnate, George Brid-

ger. "Your father is Bridger? Of Texbridge Oil?"
Instead of the admiration or wonder Miranda normally encountered when someone discovered her
identity, Clete's face took on a wary look, his eyes
narrowing as they swept over Miranda, quickly,
thoroughly. "I should have realized . . ." he murmured thoughtfully, distantly, "your clothes, your
bearing, it all fits together." Mandy sensed a certain
withdrawal in Clete, and a hot rush of anger at his
reaction suffused her like a consuming flame.

"I should never have told you!" she cried, anger
and hurt suffusing her as she fought back a stinging
sensation behind her eyelids. Fire flashed from her
eyes and she raised her chin in defiance. Even in the
far reaches of the world she could not escape her
father's influence. "It's the same old pattern," she
said bitterly. "Every time someone finds out my
name is Bridger, they either fawn all over me, or
they politely remove themselves from my presence.
No one ever takes the time or effort to know the real
me, the person inside those designer clothes, the
person who craves friendship and harbors hopes and
dreams just like any other normal woman my age!"
Miranda whirled away from Clete, her face wooden,
and stared blindly out the window. Her anger dissipated as quickly as it had come and her shoulders
slumped. She felt drained. She had not expected
such a reaction from a strong, decisive man like
Clete Montana. He had thrown her off balance,
causing her to lash out in uncharacteristic anger.
"All I ever wanted out of life," she murmured in a
strained voice, all the hurt and disappointment from
the day before welling up in her chest, "was a happy
home, a caring husband and children that symbo-

lized the commitment between their mother and father . . ." Her voice dropped to a husky whisper, and with real surprise she realized she had never before admitted those secret desires, not even to herself.

She felt Clete's persuasive hands grip her shoulders tightly yet gently. He turned her toward him and tilted her pale face upward until she was compelled to look into his dark eyes.

To her intense relief and surprise, she did not encounter pity or rejection or even skepticism at her old-fashioned and traditional desires. She could tell he was not angry at her sudden display of temper. His intelligent gaze sliced deep to find and acknowledge the person that had cried out to be recognized a few moments before. It was a heady experience for Miranda, an experience so novel that she was held spellbound, her heartbeat skyrocketing with a strange kind of elation. The moment stretched for an eternity.

"I think you misunderstood my reaction." Clete's deep voice broke the poignant silence in the room. Her eyes questioned him silently. She hoped she was not misunderstanding again. "I was just trying to fit all the pieces of the puzzle together. When you told me your father is George Bridger, everything began to make sense. Your leaving home, breaking your engagement, avoiding the man at the airport . . . it all makes sense when you put it in perspective. Your father is a ruthless businessman, and I've heard in certain circles better left unknown, that his ruthlessness spills over to his personal life." Clete, his voice grim, seemed to know things about her father that even she did not know. And before yesterday, she

had known even less about her dangerously powerful father.

"If your father knew where you were, he'd probably do anything to get you back." Clete made the
observation bluntly.

"You're probably already regretting bringing me
here," Miranda said, looking down at the floor
blankly.

"On the contrary. If anything, I owe George
Bridger a great debt." Miranda was brought quickly
out of her reverie and she stared up at Clete in
puzzlement.

"If it hadn't been for him and your fiancé, you
would never have taken refuge in my mother's car."
Clete looked down at Mandy, his grin lopsided and
boyish. A glow of warmth that had nothing to do
with the roaring fire in the wood stove began to
spread through her, and her mouth curved into a
sweet, shy smile.

Clete's gaze fell to her soft pink lips. Her eyes
sparkled like crystal as a delightful laugh bubbled up
and flowed out like music. It had been a long time
since she had felt so happy.

"Friends again?" Clete inquired.

With hands on hips, Mandy stepped back to
survey him in a pseudo-critical manner. "If you tell
me one more thing," she bargained seriously.

"Anything!"

"Where's the bathroom?"

Clete's chuckle warmed her heart long after he
had shown her the neat lean-to at the back of the
cabin where the bathroom was located, and when
she finished with her ablutions, she found him
outside in the crisp morning air. He was working on

the gasoline generator that operated the water pump. They exchanged comfortable smiles, their actions belying the fact that they had met less than twenty-four hours before.

"How soon before you get the pump working?" she asked as she leaned over his bent figure. The pungent odor of gasoline mixed with the scent of woodsmoke and evergreen.

"Not long, why?"

Her answer was lost in the sudden noise of the gasoline-powered generator, and she stepped back in surprise. Clete shrugged his shoulders in mute apology before turning his attention back to the water pump.

Miranda stepped away from the noise and took the opportunity to look around. A door in the lean-to opened into a shed filled with a variety of tools, saws, fishing rods and even an ancient washtub and board. She raised her eyebrows and realized she would have to wash her clothes the old-fashioned way.

Remembering that there would be no modern water heater here in the wilderness, she rummaged around in the shed until she found a pot that ideally suited her purpose. A shadow blocked out the light streaming in from the doorway. Mandy looked up to find Clete studying her, the look in his eyes hidden by the shade of the room's dark interior.

"What are you up to now?" he asked, his voice filled with amusement. The sight of him standing so tall and proud, his wide shoulders outlined by the light shining in behind him, made her heart do a crazy flip-flop. He looked breathtakingly masculine, his rough wool shirt giving him the air of a hardy woodsman, a man completely in his element. She realized that they were a man and a woman alone in the wilderness. There was probably not another human being within at least a hundred miles. She wondered wildly if Clete could hear the thundering beat of her racing heart.

"I'm going to heat some water," she explained quickly, hoping her eyes hadn't given away her thoughts.

"And just what do you intend doing with the heated water?" He did not move aside as she approached the exit, the pot swinging by the handle grasped tightly in her hand.

"The dishes," she gulped, her eyes drawn irresistibly upward to his shadowy face.

"I should have known, all that Dior and Gucci was just a façade!" He shook his head and raised a hand, running a light finger across her cheekbone and down to her chin.

Miranda laughed lightly, the action releasing the tension in her body, giving her precious moments to steady her rocketing pulses.

Clete took the pot from her hands and filled it with water at the pump, carrying it to the stove into which Miranda added wood, stirring the fire with a long black poker. As she stared into the hot flames licking at the dry logs, Miranda wondered at the feelings Clete evoked in her, feelings that sent searing flames of undefinable yearnings through her entire being.

In a series of kaleidoscopic scenes, she was assailed by memories of the day before: Clete touching his firm cheek to her soft one in his first spontaneous embrace, his husky voice when he had asked her name and, most of all, his lips on hers in that earth-shattering kiss just before they had entered his home. She felt weak all over again as she thought of each and every intimacy. Never before had she felt so cherished.

By the end of the reception, she had almost begun to feel as if she were his bride, and that undefinable yearning inside her returned in greater force. She felt like screaming at herself to stop thinking like that. She forced herself to construct a barrier in her mind so that her thoughts would not stray into the forbidden territory where she would imagine what the previous evening would have been like if she had actually taken the vows to be Clete's wife. Miranda Montana would not have slept alone in that cold bedroom as Miranda Bridger had. She would have been welcomed into her husband's bed with open arms, taken into Clete's passionate embrace and initiated into a world of ecstasy never before experienced, a world where those firm yet sensual lips would blend with hers. His experienced hands would have discovered all the womanly secrets she had saved just for him. . . .

Shocked by her own thoughts, Miranda jerked away from the stove, grazing a knuckle on the hot iron surface as she dropped a heavy piece of wood. The harsh sound invaded the homey atmosphere of the cabin.

Clete materialized at her side immediately as he reached out to help her. With reddened cheeks, Mandy recoiled, afraid of his touch and all of the forbidden feelings he evoked in her.

"I'm fine, really I am," she insisted. Quickly, she strode to the sink where a fresh bucket of water stood. She plunged her hand into the icy depths, welcoming the cold that seeped into her hand and up her arm. She wished the numbness could spread through the rest of her body to dampen the raging fires Clete Montana had unwittingly lit.

She was relieved when Clete, satisfied that she was not seriously hurt, left the cabin to check on their wood supply.

Chapter Four

As she learned more about Clete, Miranda became increasingly intrigued. His thoughtfulness was touching. By the time Miranda finished the breakfast dishes, he surprised her by filling the old-fashioned claw-footed tub in the bathroom with steamy water that looked like nothing short of heaven. She remembered she had not had a bath since the morning before, five thousand miles away!

Her eyes lit up. "You're going to spoil me, Clete!" she exclaimed with delight. She turned sparkling eyes toward him.

"If you look like that every time I draw your bath, I'll be doing it three times a day," he teased. His eyes caressed her flushed face. With a breathless laugh she hurried to her room, rummaging in her suitcase for fresh underclothes. When she slipped

into the bathroom minutes later, Clete had gone but
had left behind a stack of thin yet absorbent towels
and washcloths, complete with a bar of soap and a
tube of shampoo.

She sank into the depths of the ancient tub and
sighed with contentment as the warmth of the water
soothed her tired muscles. Closing her eyes, she
reveled in the feeling of cleanliness and allowed no
other thoughts into her mind.

"Hey, in there!" Rapping sounds at the bathroom
door awakened Miranda from her languor that was
brought about by the relaxing warmth of the bath
water.

"Mandy?" he called. "Did you float away?"

"I'm still here," she called in a light voice.

"Save me the water, will you? It'll take too long to
heat up that amount again, and I want to bank down
the fire before we leave." The intimate thought of
him using her bath water was squelched by his
second announcement.

"Leave?" Her heart stopped for a full moment.
"Where are we going?" she asked in a small voice.

"Hiking." His voice faded as he moved around
the corner to his room. Mandy's heart resumed
beating smoothly at his casual answer and with
anticipation, she rinsed herself. She stepped out
quickly and wrapped a large towel around herself in
sarong fashion.

Opening the door slightly, she peeked out and
called in a tentative voice, "Clete, what should I
wear to go hiking?"

She jerked when he answered, his low voice very
close to her ear. "Woman's eternal question, what
shall I wear?" He was lounging against the door
frame, propping himself up by a muscular shoulder

that strained against the wool fabric of his shirt as he pushed himself upright.

"Wear the same shirt and jeans you had on earlier," he said. "Do you have a windbreaker?"

Miranda shook her head. "No."

"Well, you can wear mine," he told her, peering over her head at the bathtub. "Are you done? The water's probably cooling rapidly."

"Of, of course! I didn't think!" she exclaimed. "I was really enjoying myself," she admitted by way of thanks as she grabbed up her clothes.

"Well, I didn't mean to curtail your bath. If you were enjoying yourself so much, why don't you get back in?" He swung the door open wide and met her in the entrance. Their bodies brushed against one another lightly. "I wouldn't mind the company," he added.

Her eyes widened as she realized the import of his words. He grinned lazily before she realized he was teasing her. Relaxing, she became aware that she had been holding her breath.

"You'd be surprised if I took you up on that invitation!" she teased in return and walked past him with as much dignity as she could muster. She had no inkling of how the thin cotton towel, wrapped neatly about her slender figure, showed all her curves to their best advantage.

As he walked into the bathroom and closed the door behind him, Miranda wondered if she imagined his retort, "I wouldn't be complaining, that's for sure." She shook her head, sure she had misunderstood. He had stressed the fact that they were friends, two companions that had hit it off well from the first minute they set eyes on one another. They had helped each other during a difficult crisis in each of their lives. The fact that their personalities and the things they wanted in life were completely compatible only strengthened that friendship, but in light of his infatuation with the elusive Fern, that friendship could never develop into something more lasting. But she was supposed to be getting over her disastrous relationship with Dayton, Mandy reminded herself. It wouldn't do to fall headlong into another relationship; falling in love on the rebound never worked out, not in the long run.

What was she thinking of, Miranda chastised herself, toying with the idea of falling in love so soon again? *I must be crazy,* Miranda mumbled to herself. Shivering in the wet towel, she hurriedly changed into her jeans and shirt and went outside into the bright sunlight to brush out her hair, the warmth and fresh air drying its brown length quickly. By the time Clete joined her with a windbreaker in hand, she was ready to enjoy her trip into the great outdoors.

Clete smiled at her as he took in the clean length of hair flowing down her back. After he helped her put on the light jacket, he lifted the tresses up and over the collar, disconcerting Mandy by bending his head to bury his face in the thickness of her hair. "It smells wonderful," he murmured, "but you might be more comfortable if you tied it back. There are a lot of brambles in the woods."

While he watched, Miranda divided up the mass of hair and quickly braided one length and then the other, her hands moving swiftly and surely. She reached into the pocket of the jeans she wore and produced several bands to secure the ends of the braids. Voicing his approval, Clete moved away. Miranda followed him silently along an animal trail that led past the bank of the lake. Then the path

veered sharply off into the dense forest of tall,
conical spruce trees.

It was intensely quiet in the woods, the only sound
the crackle of dry leaves and brittle branches under
their feet. On occasion, Clete would slow to hold
back wild brambles from Miranda's path. He helped
her walk under low-hanging branches or over a
fallen trunk of cottonwood or aspen. The path rose
gradually but steadily. Once in a while, Clete drew
Miranda close to his slim but well-muscled frame to
point out a moose or a small gopher scurrying from
place to place that froze with inquisitiveness for an
instant before rushing off to continue life's never-
ending work.

Miranda was feeling slightly out of breath as they
neared the summit of the trail, but Clete wasn't even
breathing hard. As they broke out of the forest at the
crest of the hill, they were met by the amazing
panorama of snow-tipped mountains rising and dipping on the horizon. Directly in front of them, the
ground dropped off sharply with silvery lichen,
down-soft moss and hyacinth blue harebell clinging
tenaciously to their rocky home. Several hundred
yards below, a surging river foamed and churned its
way through rock walls that guided the river on its
torturous journey to the sea many hundreds of miles
away.

Far beyond them, Miranda could see the same
river cascading sharply over white shimmering wa-
terfalls, its thunderous roar reaching them even
where they watched. Clete and Miranda stood admiring the view.

Then, Clete took Miranda's hand and led her
away from the edge of the mountain. They returned
once more to the silence of the forest. This time their

trek led them to a sunlit meadow filled with flowers. Wild poppies and roses abounded among smaller dogwoodlike blooms nestling close to the cool earth.

Clete eased himself into a sitting position to make a bench of a fallen cottonwood trunk, silver and smooth from the harsh eroding elements of the northland. Miranda sank down onto the sun-warmed grasses with a deep sigh of contentment. They had scarcely spoken five words in the few hours they had been walking. Both were unwilling to break the spell of their timeless surroundings.

Miranda gazed languorously at the blue sky and the fluffy white clouds drifting across her line of vision and fell into a state of drowsy contentment. But Clete was not about to let her fall asleep, she realized as his handsome face loomed into her line of sight.

"Oh, no, you don't." He grinned. "Get up, lazybones, we have a long way to go, and if you fall asleep now, I'll end up carrying you home."

"That sounds like a winner," Mandy answered as she stifled a yawn.

"I can feel my back aching already," he objected. "Sit up and have a candy bar. It'll give you the energy you need for the return trip." He handed her a small candy bar produced from one of his pockets. She sat up and shifted to brace her shoulders against the tree trunk.

As they savored the chocolate, Clete told her about the river whose roar was now a soothing murmur in the distance.

"Down river, about seven or eight miles from here, the river widens to an alluvial plain. Every summer my two grandfathers would go there to pan for gold."

Miranda looked up at him with interest. "Both your grandfathers knew one another?"

"Yes, together they founded Montana-Hudson Mining. That was over fifty years ago. They were called 'Monty' and 'Hud' in those days, and their fathers before them had come to Alaska during the great gold rush of 1898. Hud's father had climbed up over the Chilkoot Pass from Skagway and met up with Monty's dad prospecting down the Tanana River. From there they teamed up and went on to Kuskokwim and Susitna. They managed to survive the winter trails and the long, cold nights, escaping avalanches in the winter and floods in the break-ups that followed. They were stalwart men with the vitality and fortitude to succeed. And they did, too," Clete went on proudly. "My two grandfathers, Hud and Monty, stayed on to build a life in this harsh land, as did their sons after them." Clete smiled in remembrance. "They were two of the most delightful old codgers you'd ever hope to meet!"

Unconsciously Miranda had shifted her position on the ground to rest her chin comfortably on Clete's denim-clad knee. The fresh aroma of his sun-dried cotton jeans mingled with the earthy aroma of crushed grasses and mosses beneath her.

"Tell me about them," she encouraged.

"To a small boy, they were all the stuff heroes were made of, virile, lusty men full of life and stories, always ready to tell me stories. I guess you could say they spoiled me. The thing that impressed me most about them, and still does, is the fact that they were friends until the day they died. That's not to say they didn't have differences, because they could argue with the best of them, each other included!" Clete smiled as the fingers of one hand played with her hair, absently twisting one thick braid as he painted his picture of the pioneer men who were his grandfathers.

"As you've probably surmised, Hud was my mother's father, and Elizabeth is very much like him. She married Monty's only son, Charles, my father. The devotion of the two old men was reflected by my parents. My mother and father were more than just husband and wife; they were one another's best friends and were devoted to each other all their lives. When my father died, it just tore me apart to see my mother deteriorate right before my eyes." Mandy's heart went out to Clete, yet it was warming to see the affection and admiration he held for his parents.

"Thank you for telling me about your family, Clete. It gives me a better understanding of you." She sat up, but left a slender wrist draped across his knee as she pondered the look on his face. "It makes me realize why you wanted me to masquerade as your wife. You didn't want your mother to face even more disappointment. That spark of life in her eyes yesterday was really worth it!" she exclaimed without thinking. "Bringing new life to your family, your wife and children to carry on the Montana-Hudson family traditions is just what she needs!"

Miranda felt like biting her tongue out the minute she voiced her impulsive thoughts, for as she spoke, the easy camaraderie they had shared disappeared in the blink of Clete's eyelashes.

He grabbed her right wrist tightly, and as he drew himself to his full height, he brought her up with

him. Pulling her close to his steely length, he bent his
dark head to look down at her. A sardonic smile
twisted his well-shaped lips. "If you're thinking of
Fern Cassidy, she certainly didn't fit the part of
loving wife and devoted mother," he said angrily.
"Anyone would be a fool to ever think she cared
about anyone but herself—" His brown eyes were
almost a clear gold, an effect of the slanting sunlight
on his face. A thick lock of raven hair had fallen
onto his forehead. Mandy gave him a solemn look as
she reached out to smooth back his hair with her free
hand. What was bothering Clete? she wondered.
Had he ever contemplated making Fern his wife? He
had never actually given her the details of what had
really happened prior to his arrival back home
without the bride Elizabeth expected. Miranda
dropped her left hand away from where she had
touched his face.

The telltale pulse in her throat fluttered out of
control. He was looking at her intently. She was sure
he was fully aware of the effect he had on her every
time she touched him. She held herself rigid, almost
afraid of what he might do.

Suddenly, he released her as quickly as she had
been captured. "Don't talk about things you know
nothing about, Mandy Bridger!" Spellbound, she
shook her head, unsure of what she was denying.

"Oh, blast it all, I'm sorry!" The intense look on
his face faded in one contrite moment. "I don't
know what's gotten into me." He took her hand
back in his, pressing her fingers in a gentle, reassuring manner.

"It's not my place to speculate about someone
else's private affairs," she apologized. "It was your
turn to let off some steam. I certainly did my share of

ranting and raving this morning." She smiled ruefully and was glad to see a less disturbed light in his eyes. They were distracted by the shrill chatter of a chipmunk standing vigil on a log about ten feet away.

"See what you've done, Clete Montana," Mandy chastised him softly. "You've disturbed his afternoon nap!" They grinned at the indignant animal and, hand in hand, turned homeward.

True to his word, Clete cooked dinner and Mandy cleaned up. Since the sun set at such a late hour, they had time to take a companionable stroll along the lakeshore. Clete double-checked the moorings on the seaplane while Miranda kept a sharp eye out for the variety of animals that visited the shore nightly.

"I wish I had a camera," she lamented as Clete jumped off the wooden dock to join her. They watched the pewter-sheened lake turn rosy from the sky above, the spectacular display of colors reflected in the tranquil waters.

"I spent an entire summer here when I was a teenager. I must have taken three dozen rolls of slides. I've always wanted to come back in the winter to do more photography but I've never had the time."

They strolled side by side over the mossy banks. The serenity was broken only by the soft splash of an occasional fish jumping out of the water. When the sun finally dipped behind the mountain in the west, the famed Alaskan mosquitoes swarmed about Clete and Mandy and quickly drove them inside.

Shutting the cabin door with a hurried bang, Clete laughed. "I'll bet you don't have mosquitoes that big in Texas!" It was a direct challenge, one to which Mandy was forced to concede.

"You're right this time—I can't think of a single place in Texas where I've encountered them that big or that ferocious." She punctuated her admission with a resounding slap as she swatted at an uninvited insect that bit into the tender flesh of her arm.

"Oh, come on, you gave up too easily on that one. Can't you show even a token form of resistance?" Clete complained.

"No," Mandy answered as she stifled a yawn, "I'm too bushed to argue about anything tonight. I hope you don't mind if I turn in now."

In the dim light of the room, she saw him shake his head. "I don't mind." Courteously he lit her a candle and bid her a quiet "good night" as she closed her bedroom door.

An hour later, unable to sleep despite her weariness, Mandy slipped out of bed to tiptoe across the cold wooden floor. She cracked the door open the tiniest bit, wondering if Clete had gone to bed yet.

In the flickering candlelight she saw his seated figure. His dark shape cast a looming shadow across the room. For a moment she thought he was asleep, but then he moved to raise a cigarette to his mouth. He blew out the smoke in a long, sighing breath as he stared pensively out the window.

Closing her door, Mandy went back to bed. Was he sorry now that Fern wasn't here with him in their honeymoon cabin? Miranda wondered if they had really been on their way to their wedding, as Elizabeth had thought. If so, what had happened to change their plans? Thankfully, Miranda's tired senses finally succumbed to welcomed sleep.

* * *

The next day's activities set the pattern for the next week. Clete rose early each morning to take his fishing rod in hand, more often than not arriving back at the cabin with fresh grayling or rainbow trout for their breakfast. Miranda never offered to go with him for she sensed that he needed time alone with his thoughts. She had no intention of wearing out her welcome, and consequently took some quiet time for herself each afternoon. Her parting comment was "Carry on as if I weren't even here, Clete." She never wandered far from the cabin but stayed on the path that closely followed the lakeshore. It was comforting to walk alone, the only sound the companionable echo of Clete's ax splitting logs. Without exception, she would step into the sunlit clearing directly across the lake from the cabin, and Clete would pause in his work to wave cheerily. Then Mandy would continue on her way, happy that everything was harmonious in their private world.

At dinner time they relieved their diet of fish with the canned meats that Adam had packed in their supplies. Mandy was amazed at the variety of foods that came canned or dried, packaged in special foil pouches. Her talents in the kitchen were rapidly improving. Now that she had someone appreciative of her talents, she took to housewifely duties eagerly and enjoyed the satisfied feeling of a job well done.

She cleaned and polished everything in sight, washing the bright cotton gingham curtains on the windows, polishing the glass in every pane, never once accepting Clete's proffered help. When those tasks were completed, she left the gleaming interior behind and began on the small yard. She weeded around the base of the cabin and transplanted wild violets and clumps of poppies to create rustic flowerbeds. She used a scythe to cut down the tall grasses that were encroaching on their small space of civilization. When she asked Clete how to get up on the roof to cut the grass growing rampant above their heads, he firmly told her he would take the responsibility for that job. He had the roof neatly trimmed a few hours later. It gave Mandy great satisfaction to stand across the lake every afternoon and survey the neat cabin nestling on the slight rise of land above the lake. The structure's reflection wavered as a mountain breeze disturbed the surface of the water. The little floatplane bobbed up and down as it strained at its tethers, waiting patiently for the time to take them away from their wilderness retreat.

That was something Miranda refused to think about—leaving this place that she had grown to love. She felt safe here, and protected, even though she fully understood that it was a false sense of security. She had run away from things, from people who had hurt her, and she knew that someday those things would have to be faced. But just for now, she clung tenaciously to the small piece of heaven that Clete allowed her to share with him.

Clete . . . he was another subject that she was afraid to meet head on. She knew now that she had never loved Dayton. Their engagement had been a mistake and she was sure she could never have gone through with their wedding. There had been no spark, no deep awareness or companionship between them. The only thing they had had in common was Texbridge Oil, and Miranda seldom missed her job. It was a dangerous thought, but she admitted to herself that she much preferred doing things with and for Clete Montana.

One afternoon, Miranda was out walking, and, inevitably, she thought about Clete. At first she had tried to deny the wandering of her mind, but now she could no longer fight it. Clete was always there, filling her thoughts night and day. A light smile played at the corners of her mouth as she stopped at the clearing across the lake from the cabin. Her eyes eagerly sought his familiar figure. Clete was taking a break from his work, and she watched him as he sat on a stack of logs, the smoke from his cigarette almost invisible from where she stood. He lifted a hand in response to her greeting.

He stood up and motioned at something behind her. She glanced back into the dense underbrush of the forest, but saw nothing. Clete was waving frantically as he moved closer to the opposite shore. She remembered his warning to watch out for bears, for this was the time of the year when mother bears were out with their cubs. Clete had told her about the brown bears that were spread in good numbers over the entire state. They fed on the spawning salmon in streams and rivers and roamed stretches of secluded mountains.

Miranda jumped as she heard a thrashing in a dense thicket of paper birch a few hundred yards around the curve of the shore. She couldn't see around a fallen cottonwood tree with its uprooted shape resting half in and half out of the water.

The noise in the underbrush came closer to where she stood riveted to the ground, and she caught a glimpse of something brown moving through the trees. Clete was still motioning to her as he pointed to something beyond the cottonwood tree.

It had to be a bear. Why else would Clete be waving at her like that? Miranda panicked at the thought and began to run down the path, determined to get away from the wild animal, to reach the safety of Clete's cabin. Her hair streamed out like a banner of brown silk as she ran as fast as she could. She tripped over roots of trees and caught her hands on brambles that impeded her progress, slowing her flight homeward. Through the branches of young cottonwood trees growing close to the shore, she saw Clete's blurred figure as he sprinted in her direction. Breathing hard, she knew she wouldn't be safe until she was wrapped in the solid comfort of his protecting arms.

Miranda's heartbeat thundered in her ears, and her breath rasped harshly in her throat. She was too afraid to look back to see if the bear was following. She was not expecting Clete to appear so soon around a sharp bend in the path. Their bodies collided, nearly knocking the breath out of her. His hands gripped her shoulders and steadied her.

"Mandy . . . are you all right?" Clete's arms gathered her up and held her close for a long moment. She rested her head on his wide, muscular chest, his rapid heartbeat sounding like music to her ears.

When she finally caught her breath, she looked up to meet his puzzled gaze. "What happened?" he asked. His hands massaged her shoulders in an unconscious but gentle motion.

"The bear . . . !" she exclaimed with wide eyes.

"Bear? What bear?"

Mandy took a hesitant step backward. "I saw

. . . I heard it in the bushes . . . the brown fur . . ."
She took another deep breath and forced herself to
speak calmly and clearly. "You were pointing to the
bear in the woods, warning me . . . weren't you?"

Clete looked down at Miranda. Amusement
showed in his eyes and his mouth twitched as he tried
unsuccessfully not to laugh.

"No, I wanted you to notice our new neighbors, a
family of beavers," he explained. "They're moving
into that cove around the bend from the cottonwood
tree. That's probably what you heard in the underbrush."

Miranda felt foolish, but as she thought of her
awkward flight through the woods, her mouth
curved upward. In the next moment, she and Clete
were chuckling over her mistake.

"That's okay, Mandy," he reassured her as the
path they followed led out of the woods, "at least
you heeded my warning without question. If it had
been a bear, there would have been no time to
demand a full explanation. Under the circumstances,
you did the right thing, honey." Miranda's pulse
fluttered at the casual endearment. When he pushed
her down on the rough-hewn log bench outside the
front door of the cabin, he surprised her by dropping
a light kiss on the tip of her nose. "Stay here while I
get the first aid kit to clean up those scratches." She
had not even noticed the long red welts on her wrists
and hands. Her heartbeat had resumed its former
hectic pace and this time it had nothing to do with
wild bears or inquisitive beavers.

The next morning, Clete suggested that they pack
a picnic lunch and hike to a favorite creekbed for a
gem hunt. He had mentioned before that the Tal-

keetna mountain range was an area rich in minerals and gems. As they set off bright and early, each equipped with a prospector's hammer, he began to lecture her on the hunting process. Miranda wondered why she had never told him of her own geological training in the petroleum field. Handling a prospector's hammer was hardly a new experience for her.

Later, as they wandered along the wide rocky riverbed, picking up interesting-looking rocks, she surprised him with her intelligent observations, winning praise at the way she wielded the hammer.

"I took a few courses in mineralogy in college," Miranda admitted as she bent to pick up another rock. He had no idea that she was a petroleum engineer, and for some inexplicable reason, she did not want to tell him yet. Quickly she turned the conversation away from herself.

"I suppose gems and minerals would be the logical hobby for a boy from a family of miners." She smiled. "I'll bet Hud and Monty encouraged your interest."

The gravel crunched under their booted feet. The sound mingled with the bubbling and splashing of the creek as it curved through the wide valley. Flocks of birds winged overhead and called to one another companionably.

"You guessed it," Clete grinned, his eyes all the while trained on the rocky path beneath his feet. He bent and expertly chipped away at a rock. Straightening, he showed her his brightly colored find.

"What kind of mining does Montana-Hudson do?" she asked.

"We mine copper, zinc, lead, silver and even a

little gold," he explained as they proceeded upriver. "Right now we've been concentrating on developing some properties in the Brooks Range, particularly an open pit copper deposit."

"Does that mean you're out in the field quite a bit?"

"Yes, mostly in the summer." He caught her look, reading the question in her eyes easily. "I shifted the bulk of my work to my assistant with the promise that I'd do my share of the work later in the summer while he takes time off. I'm not totally indispensable," he smiled. "The company's set up to operate smoothly in my absence, at least for a certain while."

"I'm glad," she answered. "I'm not ready to go back yet."

Clete flashed Miranda an intense look. "I'm not ready yet either," he said slowly and seriously, his eyes filling with a disturbing awareness. Mandy glanced down to pretend an interest in the rocks at her feet, but her speeding pulse belied her outwardly calm demeanor.

"My mother inherited a jade mine from Hud and Monty," Clete went on to alleviate the pregnant silence that had fallen between them. "They used to go up to the Kobuk region north of the Arctic Circle to work in the mine. That was their idea of a vacation. They'd bring back boxes filled with slabs of the stuff. When we get back to Anchorage, I'll have Mother show you some of the jewelry she's had made from her mine."

"Oh, I'd love to see them," she explained, excited not so much at the prospect of seeing the jewelry but in the knowledge that he intended to keep on seeing her once they left their Talkeetna mountain retreat.

She was more than cheerful the rest of the day, her spirits jubilant, her energy high, and she and Clete thoroughly enjoyed their gem-hunting expedition.

Later that week, when three young hikers descended on them late one afternoon, it seemed as if their retreat were being invaded by an army. It had been so quiet, so thoroughly satisfying with just one another for company.

Clad in durable wool slacks, short-sleeved shirts and heavy boots, the three hikers were robust, cheerful young men just a few years Mandy's junior. She and Clete greeted them with hospitable smiles. Amid relieved sighs, they rid themselves of their backpacks and lowered their gear thankfully to the ground. Sweat beaded their deeply tanned brows.

Clete shook hands with each young man as they in turn introduced themselves. "Can I get you some water to drink?" Miranda inquired after Clete introduced her.

They eagerly nodded their thanks, and Miranda left Clete to inquire as to their destination. The day was exceptionally warm, not ideal for hiking and, as Miranda returned with the icy drinking water, she heard their leader asking permission to camp at the lakeshore overnight. Clete obligingly agreed. The newcomers were a cheerful, animated trio of college students eager to talk about any subject. Before Miranda realized it, she had invited them to dinner.

After they had picked out a suitable campsite, they departed to erect their lightweight tents. Miranda turned to Clete with a sudden thought. "I hope you don't mind that I invited them."

"No," he answered slowly, almost as if he were mulling over her actions for himself. "It'll do us both some good to have company," he reassured her despite an unfathomable look in his eyes. "Come on, since we have company, I'll help with kitchen duty tonight."

Dinner was enjoyable, if a bit noisier than Clete and Mandy were accustomed to. Their leader, Derek, was an open, gregarious person. Miranda found herself laughing at his exaggerated tales of their hiking trip. She knew full well that Derek padded his adventures for her benefit. She was aware, too, of his admiring glances and lingering looks, but did not take them seriously. At the same time she was troubled by Clete's unusually quiet mood. It compelled Miranda to be extra cheerful with lighthearted, bantering responses, hoping their guests would not notice Clete's attitude.

They had eaten dinner outside on a picnic table in the front yard with the lake and mountains as a beautiful backdrop. All four men had helped with the cleanup chores and soon after the sun disappeared on the western horizon, their guests departed. A blissful silence descended over the clearing once more, and while Miranda had enjoyed the youthful company of their guests, she was eager to be alone with Clete once more.

Inside the cabin, the air was hot and stuffy, and Mandy wandered outdoors once more while the fire in the stove died down. Clete busied himself opening the warped bedroom windows for extra ventilation.

Derek's stealthy footsteps gave Miranda no advance warning of his presence. He loomed beside her in the late evening shadows.

"Oh, you startled me, Derek!" Miranda exclaimed as she looked up.

"I wanted to thank you for a delicious meal." His

teeth flashed white in the gloom. He stepped much too close to her.

"But you already thanked me," she protested as she moved backwards.

"Then come talk to me," he murmured and pulled her down on the log bench. "It's been ages since I've seen a beautiful woman." Miranda had to stop herself from laughing out loud at Derek's unimaginative approach. "Where's Clete?"

"He's . . . he's in the bedroom."

"Good, that gives us a chance to get better acquainted, Mandy." Derek drew her to him so quickly that she had no time to object. She sensed that he was an expert in the art of kissing, but Mandy refused to open her mouth to his. Disgruntled, he finally released her.

"What's the matter?" he asked, puzzled.

Mandy shook her head. "You shouldn't have done that, Derek."

"Why not?" How could she tell him that he didn't appeal to her, that his kisses were lacking that certain spark. "You're not married, are you? I mean, you're not wearing a ring."

"Oh! Well . . . you see, this is Clete's honeymoon cabin . . . we came here directly from our wedding reception." She was telling Derek the truth.

"I'm sorry, I misunderstood!" He jumped to his feet quickly. "You seemed so friendly. I hope I didn't offend you. . . ."

When she assured him that he hadn't, he stood up, murmured a hurried good night and disappeared into the shadows.

Miranda sighed with relief and turned to enter the darkened cabin, wondering where Clete had disappeared to. A match flared and Clete lit a candle as she stepped inside. It startled her. He stared grimly across the room before he moved past her with quick steps to close the door. Then he grabbed her by the wrist and spun her around mercilessly.

"He may not have offended you," he growled, "but your young friend's actions certainly didn't set well with me!" His brown eyes reflected the flame of the solitary candle. As he pulled her irrevocably toward him, their shadows leaped and blended into one. He held her trapped against him, his solid flesh as hard as tempered steel. Miranda felt his breath hot on her forehead. "Not that I blame him. You look as though you enjoyed his kiss!"

"How can you say such a thing!" Miranda protested.

"If you could only see yourself, Mandy." One hand moved upward as he spoke. "Your eyes sparkle like burnished pewter, your cheeks glow like a sunset promising a warm night." His finger traced over her eyebrow and lingered on her cheek to give his words emphasis. "And your lips," his voice faded to a husky murmur, "a man could easily become addicted . . ." His mouth took hers with a wild, primitive force. His touch kindled a fire in Miranda, a fire that had been smoldering since they had met. Her hands moved upward as his kiss intensified; her fingers reveled in the thickness of his dark hair. Miranda found herself opening her mouth under his assault. She craved the rough touch of his tongue on hers. At that moment she became fully awakened to the fact that she loved Clete and would not be satisfied with anything less than complete fulfillment. The truth shook her with hurricane force.

Clete's lips released her mouth only to roam hungrily across her cheek to her shell-shaped ear.

The erotic touch of his tongue on the delicate skin left her wanting more and more. . . .

Her fingers moved to memorize the hard line of his jaw, then they wrapped themselves once more around the strong column of his neck. His lips continued their discovery of her face, moving across her lowered lids with a tenderness that belied the inferno consuming them both. Miranda discovered that he had taken his shirt off and she wondered that she hadn't noticed earlier. With a smothered exclamation, she buried her lips in the crisp furring across his chest as her fingers blazed a trail over his burning skin.

"Oh, Mandy, Mandy . . ." He sounded as if he were in great agony as he pulled away from her and thrust himself across the room.

Miranda was stunned. Tears sprang to her eyes. She forced them wide open and willed the tears not to fall and give her away.

"What did I do wrong, Clete?" she cried, her own voice low and husky from newly awakened desire.

"Wrong!" he exclaimed scornfully. "All of a sudden you're throwing yourself at every man within your reach!"

Miranda trembled as unfulfilled passion turned to anger at his unjust words. "I have not been throwing myself at every man within my reach!"

"What was your performance at dinner all about then?" His eyes smoldered with emotion.

"You were so quiet—I wanted them to feel welcome! Derek misunderstood, just like you are now! I was just being friendly!"

"Go to bed, Mandy!" Clete ordered sharply.

"But Clete, I want to explain. . . ."

"I am not made of stone, Mandy. I am a flesh and

blood man who has spent over a week alone with an attractive, desirable woman! Go to bed before I teach you the consequences of being too friendly!" His carefully controlled voice was icy with meaning yet his eyes burned like hot coals.

With her heart hammering in her chest, Miranda fled to her solitary bed, his words ringing in her ears.

Chapter Five

The next morning Miranda woke up with a throbbing headache at her temples, and by the time she stumbled out of the bathroom fully dressed in slacks and tee shirt, she realized it was past noon. The cabin was blissfully cool inside, the fire long since banked. Wondering where Clete was, she stepped outside the front door. She winced from the dull glare of the overcast sky. There was a heavy darkness on the horizon that portended rainy weather, something they had not had since their arrival. The weather suited her mood.

Abruptly, Clete walked around the corner of the building. She noted the immediate tightening of his sensual lower lip as her eyes clung to his mouth. It had been so warm, no, hot against hers and he had admitted he found her desirable. But not now. His manner was decidedly cool, despite his concentrated effort to be distantly friendly.

"Our company decided to try to beat the weather and set out at the crack of dawn," he told her. Miranda turned away, glad that they had left, almost resenting the outside interference that had spoiled her Shangri-la. If they hadn't come, she and Clete would still be good friends. "I'll get lunch as soon as I get a supply of wood in a dry place," Clete added. "No telling how long this rainy weather could last."

"I just need coffee," she murmured. "I can get it." She turned back into the cabin and left him to his job.

By the time he entered the cabin from the rear entrance, stomping his feet to rid his shoes of dirt and splinters of wood, she had the fire built up and coffee bubbling on the stove. Compared to yesterday's weather, it was decidedly chilly. Just like Clete, she couldn't help thinking.

"Do you have any aspirin?" she inquired, hoping her voice sounded normal. He hadn't mentioned last night so she surmised he would not like to resurrect that discussion. She would try to carry on as usual.

"Headache?" he inquired almost solicitously, before disappearing to find his first aid kit. When he returned he handed her two aspirin. "It's probably the weather," he said in a conciliatory tone. And that was probably as close to an apology she would get, Mandy realized. Thanking him quietly, she turned away for a glass of water.

The weather didn't keep them inside for long, a fact for which Miranda was thankful. Clete's manner remained too cool to bear for long, so in an effort to reestablish their relationship, she resumed all her old habits. She worked in the flowerbeds and walked around the lake in the afternoon. The family of industrious beavers was busy building their dam, so she altered her route slightly in an effort not to disturb them. Consequently, she bypassed the meadow where she had always stopped to wave to Clete.

An electric atmosphere began building in the cabin, slowly but surely. The tenseness between Miranda and Clete was so thick she felt she could cut it with a knife. If she had known how to alleviate it, she would have, for she could hardly bear the distance he kept between them, the polite barrier of coolness he had erected. Those first few weeks with Clete had been the happiest times of her life. Had they already become her past?

One morning Clete took his shotgun and informed her he would be gone for the day. "The season on spruce grouse opens today," he commented. "How would you like some variety in our meals?" He smiled slightly.

"Sounds good to me," Miranda responded, glad to see him acting more like his old self. "Will you be gone long?"

"I don't know. I go after the grouse in a boggy area quite a few miles from here. They feed on lowbush cranberry this time of year. I'll see if I can't flush some birds out. Will you be all right here alone?"

Miranda smiled. "Of course. I'll stick close to the house, if it will make you feel better."

"It would," he said, his eyes serious. Then he looked away quickly. "I set my handgun out for you. If you need me, fire three shots in rapid succession. I'll hear it. And the rifle is loaded in case of bears."

"Thank you, but I'm sure I won't have to use them. Can I pack you a lunch?"

Mandy was happy when he agreed, and she quickly and efficiently gathered up a substantial snack for him to take along. He even laughed when he noted how much she had packed. "That's enough for several days' time! I hope you have more faith in my hunting abilities than that!"

Miranda smiled shyly at him, her mouth curving in a slow, sweet smile. Clete's smile faded as he looked at her for a long aware moment. Then he whirled away, his light mood quickly a thing of the past.

"I'll see you later." Miranda ran after Clete but as she halted in the doorway, she saw him disappear into a thick stand of spruce.

Miranda sighed and turned to do what little housework there was, finishing up too rapidly. When she went outside later, she saw that the sun had broken through the clouds, blue peeking through the gradually clearing overcast sky. The day warmed up rapidly and Miranda sauntered to the edge of the lake and absently searched for flat stones, sending them skipping across the mirrorlike surface of the water. She wandered over to the dock. The boards were spotted with moisture where the sun gradually dried the rough wood. Her footsteps sounded hollow as she walked farther out and checked the tethers of the floatplane. It was beginning to look like an old friend, she thought as she patted its wing.

A fish splashed out of the water. The sound echoed over the lonely lake. A bird called to its mate. Mandy made her way down to the wood dock and kneeled by the edge to gaze solemnly at her reflection. Had she changed much? she wondered. She ran her hands thoughtfully over the contours of her face. Was it all too obvious to Clete that she was in love with him?

Suddenly she was jolted forward. A loose board beneath her gave way and she plunged head first into the lake. The water was deeper than it had looked. It took her several seconds to come up sputtering and feeling foolish.

She had just turned toward the shore when she felt a firm hand on her shoulder. She looked around to see Clete, fully clad, standing almost submerged in the water. "What on earth are you doing here?" she demanded.

"I could well ask you the same question," he said with barely controlled amusement in his voice. Still gripping her shoulder, he pulled her forcefully toward the grassy shore, both of them slipping and sliding on the mud near the bank.

"Hey, wait a minute—" Miranda protested before they both fell in an untidy tangle of wet clothes and humanity on the bank. Miranda was breathing hard. The full swell of her breasts strained against the cotton tee shirt that was plastered to her like a second skin.

"I thought you needed rescuing." Clete was grinning, his brown eyes twinkling down at her before roving unashamedly over her wet form, his attention lingering at her narrow waist before moving upward. His smoldering gaze caressed the dark tips of her breasts visible beneath the wet, clingy cotton. Then his eyes returned to her face, and before she could anticipate the action, he lowered his head, his mouth finding and molding its hard masculine shape to the soft curves of her lips. His kiss was hard and hungry with a ravenous ardor that sent her mind spinning and her senses reeling.

When he finally raised his head, Miranda reached out a trembling hand to caress his cheek as if she needed reassurance of his presence.

"I couldn't stay away," Clete murmured thickly. "Halfway to the river I decided I couldn't stand the situation between us any longer." Slowly, the tension in his face lessened and then dissolved completely. As she watched him, Mandy's face lit up with a happiness that threatened to spill over.

"Then we're friends again," she stated in husky triumph. Laughter bubbled up inside her. "Oh, Clete, you should see yourself! I . . . I got mud all over your face!" She held up the hand that had minutes ago caressed his face. It was streaked with mud. She moved it toward his face as if to demonstrate once more.

He pulled away quickly. "Oh, no, you don't!" he exclaimed, and laughing, he pulled them both to their feet. Their sodden clothes dripped muddy water onto the grassy shore. Miranda suddenly became conscious of how her wet clothes, in particular her shirt, clung to her figure. The wet material outlined her high, well-rounded breasts, and Clete's eyes missed nothing in his all-encompassing scrutiny, his potent gaze almost a physical touch. Mandy quivered as a lazy heat shot through her veins like molten lava.

Clete misunderstood her shiver and was immediately contrite. "You're going to catch cold! Come on, I think a hot bath is in order."

"Get out of those wet clothes," he ordered as soon as they entered the cabin, "and wrap up in a blanket until I get the water going." He strode into his bedroom, reappearing quickly and wearing a thick toweling robe. He set about heating water on the stove in a businesslike manner.

From the privacy of her bedroom, she heard him filling the ancient bathtub with buckets of heated water. Mandy shivered as she slowly stripped off the wet clothes that clung tenaciously to her cooling skin. Finding an extra blanket, she flung its length around her in sarong fashion. In anticipation, she hurried to the bathroom, closing the door firmly behind her. The blanket slipped to the floor as she whirled around, eager to sink into the warm tub. Miranda halted in midstride, a surprised sound dying on her lips. Her eyes widened at the sight of Clete reposing in the soapy water. His dark head was tilted back, lounging on the wide edge of porcelain. He grinned as she stepped back in stunned surprise.

"I don't mind sharing the water," he murmured, his eyes indolently surveying her naked form, which was frozen like an exquisite alabaster statue. Their eyes met and held for a timeless moment when everything else faded in proportion.

Finally, Mandy closed her eyes as an intensely sweet agony gripped her, filling her with an aching need. She wished she could accept his blatant offer that so tempted her. But she turned her back to him as if in denial of her desire.

She hadn't been aware that Clete had stepped from the tub. A towel was wrapped securely around his waist, soapsuds clung to his wide chest. His hands found her shoulders and he lowered his head to hers. Clete's lips roamed hungrily over the sleek curve of her neck, and a throbbing ache spread to the secret recesses of Miranda's body.

"Don't be embarrassed, Mandy." Strong hands

guided her toward the tub and gratefully she felt the soapsuds hide her vulnerable body from Clete's burning gaze. Contrary to his earlier blatant invitation, he did not join her. Instead, he picked up a bar of soap and started to lather her skin, his expert hands dissolving all vestiges of the mud. She shampooed her hair and he helped rinse its silken thickness. Miranda relaxed, as she gave herself up totally to the rapture created by his skillful hands.

"I've dreamed of this moment ever since the first time I filled this tub for you, Mandy," he whispered into her ear. His warm breath teased its tender inner skin before he moved to rub his cheek to hers like a contented cat.

Her bath finished, Clete held out a towel for Mandy, and she stepped into its softness only to find herself wrapped in the hard circle of his arms. Miranda tilted her face upward to his. Her luminous eyes flashed from beneath passion-heavy lids, her mouth curved into a sweet smile. Clete stared down at her, the expression in his eyes unreadable.

Finally he murmured thoughtfully, "You can't deny there's something between us." Miranda shook her head mutely before he continued, "We get along very well, wouldn't you agree?" This time she nodded, but wondered what he was leading up to. "We're compatible in so many ways, Mandy."

Before she could answer, he whirled away from her to throw the bathroom door open. He led her resolutely to a chair in front of the warm fire.

Under the pretext of drying her hair with a towel, he rained tantalizing kisses across the back of her neck and shoulders. Turning her toward him once more, he drew her upward into an all-encompassing embrace. His lips unerringly found hers.

It was Clete who drew away first, his chest heaving as he fought for control. "I know you're not the type of woman who'd take going to bed with a man lightly, Mandy." He observed her with hooded eyes. "I'm right, aren't I?" With a hand on her chin, he tilted her face upward, his thumb making a slow foray over her trembling lips. Her breath caught somewhere deep in her throat as she nodded in answer to his question.

"We need to talk," Clete murmured, "but you'd better get dressed first—you're much too tempting dressed the way you are." He pushed her gently toward her bedroom. "Hurry, or I'll change my mind and forget my honorable intentions!"

Mandy smiled triumphantly as she closed her door. Ten minutes later, dressed in the inevitable jeans and casual shirt, she reentered the kitchen area to find Clete dressed in similar garb. He poured them each a cup of coffee and sat down opposite her at the table.

He was silent for a long moment. His next words, spoken quietly but very firmly, shocked her. "Marry me, Mandy."

Chapter Six

"What did you say?" She wasn't sure she had heard him right.

"I want to marry you," he answered steadily.

"Why?" It was the only question Miranda could think of asking.

"Well . . ." He seemed at a loss for words for a few seconds, but then he leaned nonchalantly back in his chair, a cup of coffee clasped easily in his strong, capable hands. "You've answered that question yourself already—" At her raised eyebrows, Clete explained, "You said yourself that I wanted to give Elizabeth something to live for, something to bring back that spark of life to her eyes."

Miranda remembered her words and nodded.

"You were right about that," he continued. "I'm at the point in my life where I'm ready to get married. I've decided I need a wife, and most of all, I want children to carry on the Montana-Hudson family." His words were blunt and matter-of-fact without the slightest trace of emotion.

"I see." Mandy gulped, trying to absorb everything.

"I seem to recall you voicing a similar desire—a caring husband and children that symbolized the commitment between their mother and father," he quoted. "Well, I'm willing to assume that commitment. I want to be the father of your children."

Miranda stared across the table at Clete, her mind trying to take in everything he was saying. She flushed as she thought of everything entailed in his fathering her children. She fought valiantly for composure as her heartbeat escalated.

"But you don't love me," she said slowly.

Carefully, Clete weighed her statement and voiced his conclusions very slowly. "I've loved the life we've shared here at the cabin. I love the thought of making love to you. I love the thought of our child." He glanced away from her for a moment. Her heart sank at his words, spoken so analytically. She wondered if he was thinking of Fern.

"We have so many things going for us, Mandy," Clete went on, "more than just the usual reason of a purely physical attraction." Something of her feelings must have shown, for then, as if realizing the manner of his proposal, he added quickly, "I've startled you, I know, but I'd try very hard to make you happy, Mandy."

A long breath escaped from between her lips. Her secret wish was coming true, and she wanted to cry "Yes, yes, yes!" immediately. "Everything you've said is true, Clete," she said slowly, not wanting to give away her eagerness. She felt she should make at least a token resistance. "We do have compatible interests, our values in life are similar, but what about Fern?" She hated to bring up the subject, but she needed to know.

"I don't think there's any need to discuss any past relationships either one of us has had. Fern is in the past, just as I assume Dayton is," he answered. She realized he wasn't going to give her any more insight into the situation than she already had. "I know all this is very sudden," Clete continued as he stood up, extending a hand to her, "but it's almost as if our very first meeting was prophetic." He smiled, pulling her breathlessly close. "You made a beautiful bride, Mandy, one any man would find hard to resist."

As if in emphasis, he took her lips with his, tenderly at first, with passion finally flaring brightly, fusing them together as if one. There was no denying the attraction between them. It had been evident from their first fateful meeting. Miranda forgot all about Fern Cassidy as a wave of intense desire swept over her.

"Say you'll marry me, Mandy," Clete demanded, his lips scarcely leaving hers before they lost themselves in the ecstasy of their embrace once more. When they eventually paused for a breath, Mandy rested her forehead on Clete's strong chin.

"Are you sure this is what you want, Clete?"

"Very sure! We'll leave tomorrow—I don't want to wait any longer than necessary to file for a marriage license!" He dropped a quick kiss on the tip of her nose before he released her, urging her to help finish up their chores in preparation for their departure. Mandy followed his lead as if in a daze.

On the dock the next morning, Miranda took a last lingering look at the cabin where she had been so happy. With everything they needed stowed in the seaplane, Clete came back to where she stood. He threw his arm around Miranda and his eyes followed hers. "We'll come again," he reassured her gently, and she smiled up at him trustingly. Together they turned and boarded the plane.

The flight homeward was spectacular. Clete pointed out the magnificent scenery of the "Great Land," as Alaskans fondly call the forty-ninth state. "I'll have you know this kind of flight is a high-cost item on most itineraries," he informed her in a teasing voice. The small plane flew over ribbons of clouds that brushed the tops of the mountains. As they crested the snow-kissed peaks, Clete pointed out the Matanuska Glacier shimmering in the eerie light like a river of molten aluminum, its advancing edge a startling aqua blue.

"People come from all over the world just to see these glaciers," he told her. Then he guided the craft downward, giving them a closer view of lush green meadows nestled in the hollows between rocky brown and gray slopes that rose into misty clouds. The plane flew onward.

"There's Hatcher Pass." Clete's attention never wavered from the countryside below them. "Gold is the Alaska State mineral, and twenty million dollars of gold was taken from those diggings." Miranda was fascinated by the sight of the deserted wood buildings of the gold mine standing as a poignant reminder of years long past. It was a ghostly sight. Weathered wood structures dotted the mountains. Old shacks clung tenaciously to the sides of plunging cliffs, and the openings of forgotten tunnels gaped in dark testimony of better days.

"It looks like some mining is still going on!" Miranda exclaimed, pointing to a few modern structures to one side of the old mine.

"With gold priced as high as it is these days, it will eventually become economically feasible to reopen more of the old mines," Clete explained.

Wisps of clouds brushed the higher ramshackle structures. Forgotten rails, used to haul away the ore, rose on broken trestles leading to nowhere. Except for several new metal roofs on the more recent buildings, the complex was a bleak study of grays and browns, slowly decaying as the green countryside reclaimed what man had once taken.

The brown ribbon of a man-made road wound its way down the mountain. Miranda watched the steely blue of a river plunge angrily over massive boulders as it cut its tortuous way through the summer countryside. The plane was low enough for her to see the miniature figures of a family picnicking in a flower-filled meadow, the father and several children panning for gold at the river's edge. The children waved up at the craft, and Clete dipped the wings from side to side in a playful salute.

They flew onward over the Matanuska Valley, where a network of farms and dairies dotted the intense green of the land. In the distance, the gray blue of Cook Inlet beckoned.

It wasn't long before Clete circled the seaplane over a familiar lake ringed with expensive homes. The plane banked in a turn and dropped to glide over the bright blue water, finally bringing the small craft to its home berth.

As he helped Miranda out of the cockpit, Clete caught her in a tight embrace and exclaimed, "Welcome home, wife!" She had never been so happy.

Clete proved a master of efficiency as he whisked Miranda through the necessary steps of acquiring a marriage license. The four-day waiting period required in Alaska passed quickly. No one knew they were back in town, and Clete jealously kept Miranda to himself. As she had already discovered, he was an interesting man, knowledgeable in a variety of subjects besides geology. They conversed long into the evenings. His sense of humor was contagious, and they laughed with one another over past misadventures, including their own fateful meeting. Miranda delighted Clete with the tale of her flight from Pace Dickinson, making it sound like a page out of a spy thriller.

Inevitably, the atmosphere between them heightened to a maddening intensity, but neither one took the step that would vault them into the next logical stage of their relationship. Clete played the ardent suitor, and she was hard-pressed to remember that their upcoming marriage was one of convenience and not of love. At least not on his part, she thought as they stood side by side in front of the minister in a picturesque wooden chapel nestled in a mountain meadow.

They repeated their vows in firm but quiet voices. When the time came for the exchange of rings, Clete surprised Miranda with a wide band of Alaskan jade, a beautiful green shot through with faint black

and gray markings. It looked as though it had been
hand carved from one solid chunk of jade, perhaps
from the Hudson mine. Miranda raised her gaze to
Clete's face. As she slipped a heavy masculine ring
of entwined Alaskan silver and gold onto his finger,
the fit was amazingly perfect. She could see that her
gift filled him with deep emotion, and his eyes
expressed profound depths that sent Miranda's pulse
skyrocketing.

When they were officially declared husband and
wife, Clete took Miranda into his arms, branding her
with a long, deep kiss of possession that kept her
warm on the ride to Anchorage.

They had their wedding supper at Clete's apartment where he surprised her with vintage champagne and a sumptuous meal catered by a prominent
restaurant. Finally alone as husband and wife,
they silently watched from the bay window as
the sun dipped low into Cook Inlet, the vivid light
outlining the ice-capped volcanoes at the very
tip of the mighty Alaska Range. Purple shadows
engulfed Miranda and Clete as they enjoyed
their meal of Alaskan king crab. The soft flames
of a candle cast romantic shadows over Miranda's
face.

Clete fingered his ring as they lingered over after-
dinner drinks. "This was a nice surprise," he admitted gruffly. Miranda smiled at her husband, all her
love shining from luminous eyes. Clete's gaze clung
to her face.

"This was a surprise, too," she responded after a
moment, holding her hand up to inspect her new
ring.

"It belonged to my grandmother. Hud had it

made from the best jade from his own mine. Does it fit?" he asked, leaning toward her.

"It's perfect." Miranda smiled, holding her hand out to show him.

"I'm glad." They smiled at one another over the flickering flame of the candle, savoring the slow but steady buildup of a tension that had existed between them from the very first moment they had met. Finally Clete stretched out his hand and guided his bride into his bedroom. Very gently, he removed her wedding garments, his eyes savoring the delights of her unclad form.

She sighed once, and then her arms welcomed Clete as he molded the entire length of his body to hers. His ardent mouth was on her lips, her neck, the rising thrust of her breasts.

"Love me, Clete!" Mandy whispered. She craved fulfillment and raised her arms to his shoulders. Obeying her, he moved his hands to her hips in guidance, lowering his lips to hers. His mouth clung to hers as together they entered a vortex of hoarded passion.

Miranda was brought to full consciousness by the gentle touch of a hand moving over the concave velvet of her stomach. She turned her head to smile drowsily at Clete, not realizing how her pearly skin glowed. Her eyes lit up in that special, secret way as she gazed over at him.

Clete propped himself up on one elbow to look down at his wife. Her brown hair spread over his pillow in tawny strands. His skillful hand roamed upward, sliding over her velvety waist, her breast swelling to meet his palm as he cupped its fullness.

He buried his face between the inviting crests, his hand moving to her flat abdomen.

When he finally raised his head, his eyes were serious and thoughtful.

"What is it, Clete?" Mandy had to make a concerted effort to keep her voice steady.

"You realize that a child . . . our child," he amended, "could be starting life, right here, right now." His hand gently caressed her stomach. A flame leaped and when his lips followed the path blazed by his hands, they lost themselves once again in love.

Much later, Miranda and Clete dressed and left the small city apartment that he explained was in the same building as his mother's penthouse suite. On the way to the elevator, Clete inquired of his wife what she would like to do for the remainder of the evening. "We should celebrate," he told her.

"Could we visit your mother?" Miranda asked. She saw that her request pleased him. He nodded and took her hand in his, leading her into the lift where he pressed the button for his mother's floor. The elevator shot them easily to the top floor of the building where Clete ushered Mandy down a well-decorated hallway to a heavily carved door.

Joyce answered the bell. When she saw Clete and Miranda, her face crumpled into an expression of abject relief.

"Oh, Mr. Clete, I'm so glad you're home!" She stepped back to allow them entry.

"Joyce, what's the matter? Is it Mother . . . ?"

"No, no, she's all right, at least she was until early

this afternoon." Joyce hesitated, doubt clouding her eyes as she looked from Clete to Miranda.

"What do you mean, is she ill?" Clete demanded.

"No, but I'm worried that she might be a little . . ." Before Joyce could explain, Elizabeth Montana heard their voices in the foyer.

"Clete? Mandy? Is that you?" Clete's mother appeared in a doorway at the far end of the carpeted hallway. She was elegantly dressed in a maroon dinner gown, and her thin hands flashed with pinpoints of light from the diamonds and sapphires of her rings.

Clete ushered Mandy down the hallway to join Elizabeth at the arched entrance to a beautifully appointed living room.

"Mother, how are you?" Clete bent to kiss his mother on the cheek, a worried frown furrowing his brow.

"Oh, stop fussing, I'm fine. Let me look at you two." She surveyed her son and his wife with satisfaction. Her sharp gaze took in the bloom of health and happiness evident on Miranda's cheeks. Her glance flitted to the possessive touch of Clete's hand on Miranda's waist. It was the touch of a man who knew his woman intimately, and by the way Miranda leaned into Clete's body, she unconsciously revealed her acknowledgment of his claim. Elizabeth's eyes flashed from face to face, and she seemed to stand straighter, but she looked concerned as she embraced Mandy, offering her cheek to her daughter-in-law for an affectionate greeting. Clete looked at the two women affectionately.

Elizabeth turned to her son with a strange hesitation. "Clete, I don't know how to break this to you . . ." She threw a quick glance at Miranda and was about to continue when a polished voice interrupted.

"Clete, darling," Fern Cassidy cried in a husky voice, "I've come back to you, so you can give our child a father!"

Chapter Seven

The redhead's carefully made-up face took on a hauntingly lovely expression as her wide blue eyes shimmered with unshed tears. With the grace of a trained dancer she moved to embrace Clete, who stood riveted to the floor, his hands moving irresistibly to Fern's tiny waist. The cloying scent of expensive perfume wafted around them in a cloud. Miranda, standing slightly behind her husband, watched their tender reunion. Stunned, she felt like an intruder on the intimate scene. All Miranda's doubts and uncertainties concerning her husband's relationship with Fern Cassidy washed over her. For the first time in her life, she felt like succumbing to a faint, but she bit back the sudden nausea welling up in her throat. Over Clete's broad shoulder, his muscles flexed beneath the fine material of his wedding suit, Fern subjected Miranda to a cold, calculated appraisal and, in the flicker of her long thick lashes, Miranda realized she had been relegated to a matter of little concern.

"Don't tell me that you're pregnant?" Clete inquired. His tone was ironic.

Miranda felt another wave of dizziness pass over her and was thankful for Elizabeth's steadying hand on her arm.

"Well," Fern hedged, pulling away from Clete with a theatrical movement designed to bring her beautifully contoured body to his attention. "Not exactly. But you said when you married, you wanted children right away. I thought you'd be interested to hear that I'm ready to settle down."

"That is very interesting," Clete replied smoothly. "What happened to that lead part you had been offered?" His question was conspicuously devoid of emotion.

Fern tossed her flyaway hair over her shoulders, drawing her willowy body to its full, ultra slender height. "The role didn't suit me," she said with casual unconcern.

"And you think the role of Mrs. Clete Montana would suit you . . . ?"

The blue eyes took on a sultry hue. "I always thought the part suited me, despite our minor differences of opinion." Miranda's heart plunged as she intercepted the long glance between Clete and Fern.

"Mother, didn't you tell Fern the news?" Clete never removed his eyes from Fern's figure.

"I thought that was best left to you," Elizabeth replied dryly.

"What news?" Fern asked lightly, a slight smile touching her full, sensual lips.

The woman looked enchanting and knew it, Miranda thought unhappily.

"I seem to have acquired a wife since the last time we met," Clete announced.

Fern's opal-bright eyes filled with surprise and dismay. But she gathered her wits together quickly and with a charming manner turned to Miranda as Clete introduced the two women. To a casual onlooker Fern appeared to concede defeat with unsurpassed dignity, but Miranda caught the steely challenge hidden behind the other woman's glittering eyes.

"Please," Elizabeth interrupted, "let's all sit down. Joyce, would you bring some drinks?" The housekeeper appeared as if by magic. "A Scotch for Clete and sherry for the ladies."

"Oh, yes," Fern cried. Long, red-tipped fingers curved around Clete's arm. "Let's toast your charming little bride."

Only Miranda caught the condescending inflection of the other woman's words. Fern led Clete resolutely to the Louis XV settee made to accommodate only two persons, leaving Miranda and Elizabeth to choose from the two armchairs flanking the mid-eighteenth century tulipwood coffee table. Miranda seated herself in an antique satin-covered beechwood fauteuil, leaving the more comfortable velvet-upholstered bergère to Elizabeth.

For a moment, an uncomfortable silence hung over the room, and Clete did nothing to alleviate the tension. His dark eyes scrutinized Fern Cassidy. The woman crossed incredibly long legs in a motion deliberately cultivated to capture masculine attention.

Miranda felt abandoned. Nervously she clasped her hands in her lap, fiddling with her jade wedding band. It should have given her some comfort to be wearing a ring that had held such meaning just a few hours before. If it hadn't been for the poignant ceremony so filled with promise earlier in the day, Miranda would have gladly run from this room, away from the stranger that Clete had suddenly become. His earlier words seemed to echo in her bruised mind—she had suddenly become an "acquisition!" An acquisition that was now an obstacle, keeping him from the bride Clete had thought was lost.

Elizabeth moved an agitated hand, the action drawing Miranda's attention, making her wonder what Clete's mother made of this new situation. Surely she must suspect that Fern was the original candidate for the status of her daughter-in-law. Was that disapproving look in Elizabeth's eyes and the tightening of the soft lips indicative of the confusion the woman must feel? She was probably wondering where Miranda fit into the picture, by now realizing that Mandy was not the woman from Las Vegas she had spoken to on the telephone just a few short weeks ago. Fern's conversation was filled with shared remembrances, her calculating comments prompting Clete to respond to the reminiscing of the time, years ago, when they had first met. Elizabeth raised her eyebrows. Clete had assured Mandy that his relationship with Fern was in the past, but the woman was now very much a part of their present. Elizabeth and Miranda shared a quick glance of relief when Joyce interrupted with the requested drinks. She set the tray in front of Elizabeth on the maroon leather-topped coffee table.

Abruptly Clete removed himself from Fern's possessive touch. A thoughtful look settled over his taut features. He shifted his position to the corner of the cane-backed settee that was elegant with its cabriole legs and velvet-upholstered seat. The three women attempted to carry on the semblance of a conversation.

"Where are you staying?" Miranda asked Fern politely after a long, uncomfortable lull in the conversation.

"Oh, Mrs. Montana has graciously welcomed me into her home, Mindy," Fern said smugly. Clete's mother threw an apologetic look at Miranda.

Miranda silently forgave Clete's mother. She realized Fern had placed Elizabeth in an impossible position.

Clete's mother rose slowly. "If you'll excuse me, Miss Cassidy, my daughter-in-law, Mandy," she pointedly lingered over the relationship, "will help me to my room. I'm feeling quite tired. I think I'd better retire for the evening." Her face was pale and strained looking. Her son was immediately contrite.

"Will you be all right, Mother? Can I help?" Clete jumped to his feet.

"No, son, your lovely wife is all the help I need. Mandy's already an indispensable member of this family," she said to Fern, smiling warmly at Miranda who advanced to take Elizabeth's thin arm. "Good night, Miss Cassidy. If you need anything else, Joyce can help you."

When the two women entered Elizabeth's bedroom, Miranda sank shakily into an easy chair.

"Here, drink this, Mandy, dear." Elizabeth thrust a small snifter of brandy into Miranda's hand. Without argument, she downed the reddish gold liquid in one gulp, gasping slightly as the potent drink burned all the way down her throat. It started a small, warming fire in her stomach, and in a few minutes she felt better.

She glanced up to see Elizabeth sitting on an upholstered bench in front of a French dressing table. She looked at Miranda with affection and concern.

"I suppose you're wondering what in the world is going on?" Miranda asked in a small voice.

"Oh, I have a pretty good idea." Elizabeth smiled. "And I must thank heaven for sparing me that odious woman as a daughter-in-law. You'll be much better for my son."

"We didn't intentionally try to deceive you, Elizabeth."

"I know, my dear, you don't have to apologize. I quickly realized after Clete got into the car that day at the airport that you two didn't know one another at all!" A reminiscent smile lingered at the corners of her lips, her dark eyes reminding Miranda of Clete. "I have to admit I was wondering how long the two of you would be willing to carry on your little deception. It was one of the most delightful afternoons I've ever spent!" She chuckled in remembrance. Then she turned serious. "You two made such a lovely couple that day, and I hoped then that you would get along. My wishes have come true, haven't they?"

Miranda felt an intense need to explain to someone just how she had come to be Clete's wife. "We started out with the idea of being just friends who were sharing a vacation, but an attraction seemed to grow between us, slowly but surely. We had both been through some rather trying experiences with the opposite sex so we had a lot in common. Finally," her eyes took on an unconsciously warm glow as she remembered, "Clete asked me to marry him. We vowed to make one another happy, to build a life together, Elizabeth," Miranda reassured his mother. "But everything seems changed now that Fern Cassidy has returned to his life." She spoke the words as much to remind herself as to explain to Elizabeth.

"You love Clete," Clete's mother observed quietly. "Well, I certainly hope my son is wise enough to see what he has in you," she added with a smile that fell short of imparting the reassurance intended.

Joyce knocked at the half-open door and slipped in at Elizabeth's indication. "Joyce, take my daughter-in-law back to her husband now, and please inform Clete and our unexpected houseguest that I expect to see them at dinner here tomorrow night." She turned to Miranda. "You and I, Mandy dear, need to get to know Miss Fern Cassidy better," she explained grimly. "It's always wise to confront the opposing forces head on and on home territory, if possible."

Miranda bid Elizabeth a fond good night and followed Joyce back to the living room where she heard Fern's throaty laugh mingling with the deeper sounds of Clete's responses. As she halted momentarily in the doorway, she caught Fern removing her hand from the curve of Clete's firm jaw. Miranda's heart ached dully.

Joyce relayed Elizabeth's invitation to dinner in a reserved voice and pointedly indicated to Fern that she, Joyce, would now show her to her room. The

three said a stilted good-bye, Fern throwing Clete a
look full of future promise, her husky words, "See
you tomorrow, darling," accompanying it. Clete
tilted his head in mute response, slipping an arm
around Miranda's slender waist. The pearly silk of
her wedding dress gave way to his cool fingers as he
guided her out of his mother's home.

As they stepped into the elevator, Mandy cast a
surreptitious glance at her husband's face. Its icy
visage frightened her, for his features were like a
carved mask of stone. Miranda had a strange premo-
nition that she would never again encounter the
warm, loving man she had married earlier that day,
the wonderfully considerate man she had lived with
in the simple cabin in the Alaskan wilderness. Cold
despair washed over her at the thought.

Clete settled Miranda in the passenger's seat of
the Mercedes and walked around the car to seat
himself behind the steering wheel.

"I'm sorry Fern had to intrude on your wedding
day, Miranda," he said kindly, and beneath his
thoughtful words she detected a hint of anger. But
all Miranda could think about at the moment was
that he referred to it as "her" wedding day and not
"theirs." Or was she being too sensitive and reading
too much meaning into just casual words?

"How . . . how long has she been here . . . in
Alaska, I mean?"

"She arrived just this afternoon." His grim tone
disheartened her. She wondered if Clete was sorry
now that he had rushed her to get their marriage
license and to go through with a wedding ceremony.
Was he wishing he had waited just one more day?

Chastising herself sharply, Miranda refused to

conjecture further on her husband's choice. He had assured her that Fern was in his past, and she had to trust him. Clete was her husband now, she reminded herself firmly. Yet, as she stared at him in the dark, he appeared to be a frightening stranger. They drove home together in silence, each lost in a world of private thoughts neither could share.

Silver moonlight fell across the carpet, washed out its color and traced a gilded path to the bed where Miranda waited for her husband. Her face was bathed by the cool celestial light, and she shivered. Would she ever feel warm again? Where was Clete? Would he still want her now that Fern was so close and so obviously available? Miranda's mind spun with a thousand contradictory thoughts, remembering everything that had occurred during the long day. A dark shadow moved across the room. The mattress gave way to Clete's solid form. Miranda was afraid to move for fear of catching his attention, perhaps forcing him to remember her presence. She held her breath for a long moment, then forced herself to breath shallowly.

Out of the corner of her eye she saw Clete run a hand over his face wearily, the moonlight outlining his features with its cold light. Did she imagine his deep sigh? Then he murmured an unintelligible expletive and she sensed his pent-up anger.

When he turned toward her, the expression in his shadowed eyes was hidden from her. His mouth came down on hers with a fierceness he had never before displayed. Was he angry because it was Miranda and not Fern in his bed on his wedding night?

His hand started to move over her body, which he had come to know so well in such a short period of time. Soon she was lost, melting under her husband's expert touch. Whatever feelings he may have harbored for the beautiful Fern had not dispelled the physical desire he inevitably displayed toward Miranda. As his mouth devoured hers, she knew with a certainty that she would never forget her wedding night.

Golden light replaced the cool reflected rays of last night's moon. Miranda blinked and realized it was morning. Instinctively she turned to Clete's side of the bed. How quickly she had come to expect the solid comfort of his presence. She smiled tenderly, but the smile faded as she realized she was alone. Pushing the tangled hair from her eyes, she slipped from the bed, her light footsteps silent on the thick green carpet. The air in the bathroom was moist from a recent shower and she detected the scent of Clete's shaving cream and the lingering aroma of his distinctive cologne. Miranda closed her eyes for a long moment, absorbing the essence of her husband's recent presence. Then the events of the previous night flooded over her, shame for succumbing so easily to him warring with resentment at herself for having truly enjoyed his calculated approach. Had he gotten up from their bed and run to Fern, fraught with guilt at desiring one woman while loving another? Miranda wished she knew more about their past relationship.

Miranda tried to put herself in Clete's place. She herself had been disillusioned by her former fiancé, but she had quickly learned that she had never loved

Dayton. Only her pride had been hurt, Miranda reflected as she returned to sit on the edge of the rumpled bed. Miranda's fateful flight from hurt had led her to Clete, the only man she would ever love. Not once had she missed her career. She had scarcely given her job a second thought. The drive and ambition she had once had was no longer important in her life—only Clete mattered to her. It was almost frightening to know that all her happiness rested in his capable hands. If he didn't want her as his wife, she would be faced with a desolate future. A shiver ran through her small frame and she rubbed absently at the jade wedding band, its presence imparting a small measure of comfort.

Taking a deep breath, she stood up and turned to check the time. A note was propped up beside the clock radio on Clete's bedside table. She had missed it in her earlier eagerness to seek him out. With a sinking heart she read that his presence was required at the office and he would not return until late afternoon. The note was signed simply "Clete."

Miranda lay down on the bed, burying her face in Clete's pillow before taking a firm hold of herself and her emotions. Then she returned to the bathroom for a warm shower. She spent the rest of the morning occupied with various household chores, making the bed, straightening the bathroom, and planning dinner. Vexed, she remembered they were to dine at Elizabeth's. Her heart filled with dread at the thought of seeing Fern Cassidy again. She didn't want to watch the beautiful redhead lure Clete away.

When she started to plan her outfit for the coming evening, she was dismayed to realize that she had no clothes suitable for dining out, other than her pearl-

colored wedding dress that Fern had already seen.
Pondering her plight, she wandered out on the deck,
stopping in the kitchen for a sandwich along the way,
combining breakfast and lunch.

The lake glistened a deep blue in the serene
afternoon and the Chugach Mountains stood high
above in stark relief. The pontoon plane floated
peacefully at its berth. She noticed that their neighbors, the Kellys, also had a seaplane similar to
Clete's. Mandy heard the laughter of the Kelly
children, the light sounds blending with the deeper
sound of their father's voice. He must have returned
from Prudhoe Bay on schedule. Miranda knew that
the oil workers north of the Arctic Circle worked
extended shifts for a full week, and then were
shuttled home to take the next week off. It was a
rigorous type of life and it took some getting used to,
especially for the families, yet there was a certain
fascination to a career in the North Slope oil fields.

Miranda turned and saw Jane saunter out on the
patio of their house next door, and the older woman
waved a greeting.

"Don't tell me Clete is back to work already?"
Jane called.

Miranda nodded and answered, "He said there
were things that only he could handle."

Jane invited Miranda over for a cup of coffee. She
accepted eagerly, realizing how nice it would be to
have an undemanding conversation with another
woman. In the cosy early American style kitchen,
Jane poured Mandy a cup of hot, dark coffee.

The two women talked companionably for a few
minutes before they were interrupted by Todd and
the children calling out a cheery good-bye.

"Todd is taking them to an afternoon matinee at the movies." Jane explained. "That way I get a break. Being mother and father to them every other week is exhausting at times, especially in the summer when school is out." She smiled ruefully. "When Todd is gone, I rarely have a minute to myself."

"Oh, but they're such lovely children," Mandy protested.

Jane laughed. "Yes, but it's hard to be a mother twenty-four hours a day, seven days a week. I know it sounds selfish, but a woman needs time for herself, even if it's just a half hour to soak in a hot tub, reading the latest romantic bestseller."

"I suppose," Miranda replied. Then she noticed the keys and handbag placed on the table. "Am I holding you up, Jane? If you were planning on going somewhere, don't let me interfere!"

"Oh, you're not interfering. I have plenty of time to go shopping. That's another thing I can't do when Todd is gone. It's really hard to try on new clothes when three kids are hanging on to your skirt!"

"I need to get some clothes soon," Mandy admitted. "I came up from Texas with very little, and I need some things suitable for evening wear. Jeans might have been fine for Clete's cabin or doing housework, but not to have dinner with my husband's very chic ex-girl friend!"

"Texas? I thought you were from Las Vegas?" Jane said, a slight frown furrowing her brow.

"Oh, well." Miranda became slightly flustered before she answered. "I'm originally from Texas. Can't you tell by my southern twang?" Jane laughed and agreed.

"Now that you mention it!" Then she continued,

dwelling no more on the puzzle of Miranda's background. "Well, if you're going to have dinner with one of Clete's ex-girl friends, we don't want you to come out second by comparison! How would you like to come downtown with me? You could get a couple of dresses at the mall I'm going to; they have the most unique clothes in town."

"I'd love to come!" She thought of the coming evening when she would be compared to the beautiful Fern. The least she could do was to be well dressed.

The two women spent the next few hours shopping in a small exclusive mall. The cluster of shops offered everything from head to toe, starting with a beauty shop and ending with exquisite designer shoes unrivaled even in Houston's international shops. Miranda had taken the time before they had left the house to slip into a comfortable denim skirt in place of her jeans, and in her handbag she carried over half of the cash she had left over from her Houston savings account, still a substantial amount.

Miranda and Jane laughed together like old friends, and both women arrived home tired but happy, their purchases carefully wrapped and boxed.

"Let me know what Clete's reaction is to your new clothes, Mandy!" was Jane's parting reply to Miranda's thanks for taking her.

Back in her bedroom, Miranda put away all her purchases: the lacy lingerie she put into the long triple dresser Clete had designated as hers, the dresses she hung in a closet large enough to be used as a dressing room, and the shoes and matching handbags she stored neatly on a spacious set of shelves inside the walk-in closet. Surveying her purchases with a satisfied gleam in her eyes, Miranda felt she was now sufficiently armed for any contingency.

Those tasks completed, Miranda had just enough time to take a relaxing bath, lavishly adding a bath oil that matched the scent of the new perfume she had bought in one of the boutiques. She was luxuriating in the tub when Clete arrived home, surprising her with a long, low whistle as he appeared in the bathroom doorway.

"What a sight for a weary husband home from a hard day's work!" His teasing grin and roving eyes caused Miranda's heart to do a crazy flip-flop. She had not known what to expect, but the familiar reassuring smile, the light in his eyes as they caressed her body with an almost physical touch, set her mind at ease.

He smiled and knelt beside the tub. "Can I join you in there?"

"I hardly think you'd like the scent of my bath oil, on you, that is!" Mandy teased him.

He bent his head in mock disappointment. "What did you do all day?" he asked, bending to brush his lips to hers in a butterfly-soft action. He straightened but continued to gaze down at her, and Miranda did not attempt to act the shy maiden and hide what he had so boldly taken the previous night.

"I . . . I accomplished a few housewifely chores, and then Jane asked me to go shopping with her. I thought my wardrobe needed some improvement, so I went along." She reached out her hands in an unspoken request, and Clete helped Mandy out of the tub, wrapping her securely in a thick towel. Then he trapped her inside the circle of his embrace.

"Well, as far as I'm concerned, you don't need clothes," he murmured, pressing his mouth to the curve of her neck. He bent and lifted her into his arms, carrying her to the bed. Quickly, he divested himself of his dark business suit and coordinating shirt and tie. Then he was beside her on the bed, his mouth taking hers with fierce ardor. He rolled over onto his back and pulled her with him so that she lay over his full length. She rested her chin on her arms that were folded over his wide muscular chest. She could feel his body beneath hers, responding to the weight and touch of her lighter one, their limbs tangling together eagerly. It was a heady feeling to be able to arouse a quickening response from such a virile man as Clete, a man well versed in the ways of women and lovemaking. He drew Miranda's lips down to cover his, and soon they were lost in their love.

"Oh, I wish we could stay here instead of going into town for dinner!" Miranda cried as the last wave of passion shuddered through her replete body. She lay with her head on Clete's muscular shoulder, his corded arms wrapped around her protectively. Instantly she wished she hadn't uttered those spontaneous words for they seemed to wash away the warmth in his golden eyes. What had she said, she wondered, biting her lower lip as he drew away from her. Clete stood up abruptly.

"I need a shower before I dress for dinner," he explained in a quiet voice before disappearing into the next room. Did he regret his relationship with Miranda because he loved another woman, a woman who had come back into his life? Miranda wanted to ask him outright, but she realized that now was not the time.

When Mandy stepped out of her dressing room wearing one of her new outfits, she knew she looked more than just attractive by Clete's quick look of astonishment. She had chosen a two-piece ensemble in a jade green and white printed silk crepe de chine. It was artfully simple, the loosely styled blouse sporting a square neckline cut to give the barest hint of the cleavage between her full breasts and the matching dirndl culottes falling softly to below the knee, giving it a skirtlike effect. A wide metallic band of gold belted her small waist, emphasizing its trimness above the graceful curve of her hips.

Her legs were encased in the sheerest of stockings and her small feet wore the latest fashion in shoes, a pair of open-toed metallic whipsnake pumps piped in gold kidskin. She carried a slim matching clutch purse.

At Clete's huskily voiced admiration, Miranda ran her small pink tongue over her lips, which were attractively full from Clete's ardent kisses. Her long brown hair fell in a dark cloud over her shoulders. Her gray eyes were large and wide with the look of recently appeased passion smoldering in their depths.

"You look lovely," Clete told her. "Is this part of the wardrobe you mentioned earlier?" His eyes darkened. "May I ask how you have been paying for all of these clothes, the wedding dress, my ring?" He fingered the gold and silver band on his left hand as if its presence disturbed him. Perhaps, Miranda thought despondently, he was one of those men who

did not want to be encumbered with a ring despite
the fact that he was married. Or perhaps now that
Fern had returned he did not like being reminded of
his married state. An ominous silence stretched
between them.

"I have a little bit of cash from my savings account
at home," she finally replied stiffly.

"Home?" His voice was icy. "A little bit, for all
this?"

"I meant Houston, Clete." She could not understand his lightning-quick mood changes. He acted
almost angry at her now. Her carefully laid plans of
dazzling him with her new clothes and sophistication
crumbled at her feet even before they had encountered the ravishing Fern Cassidy. "And the money
was from . . ." She was about to tell him of her job
as a petroleum engineer at Texbridge when he cut off
her answer with a sweeping wave of his hand.

"I don't really care where the money came from,"
he interrupted harshly. "Tomorrow we'll see that
you get your own bank account here in Anchorage,
plus I'll have your name put on my credit cards.
You're my wife, Miranda Montana, and I'll be the
one to pay for your food and clothes and whatever
else you think you need! I'm not Dayton Green, you
know, and I'll not take any proceeds that come from
your rich father, directly or indirectly! In case you
haven't realized it by now, I'm fully able to support
my high-society wife in the style and comfort you're
obviously accustomed to having!" With his jaw
muscles clenched, Clete strode from the room. Miranda stared after him in stunned confusion at his
uncharacteristic outburst. She had thought she
knew Clete fairly well when they had shared a
remote cabin in the wilderness. Yet it now

seemed that she had a lot more to learn about her husband, the man she had been married to for a scant twenty-four hours. Miranda sighed and glanced at the slender gold watch on her wrist. It was nearly time to leave. Reluctantly, she followed Clete out of the bedroom.

Chapter Eight

By the time Clete and Miranda arrived at Elizabeth's, the sun was sinking into the crimson-washed inlet, and with it fled Miranda's tenuous hold on her spirits. Clete had been silent during much of the ride over, his thoughts far away. Why had his behavior altered so radically? As the elevator whisked them smoothly and silently to the top floor, she often glanced at Clete, whose hand rested at the small of her back. It was a reminder that she belonged to him now as surely as if he had branded her with a hot iron. She was so deeply in love with him that she felt lost without his complete attention. But he was probably thinking of seeing Fern again. The thought defeated Miranda even before the door was opened by Fern, resplendent in a clinging black gown with a high-necked, sleeveless top that empha-

sized her wide, tanned shoulders. She exuded a
sophistication and worldliness to which Miranda
could never aspire. Mandy felt like a little girl in her
jade green culottes that so perfectly matched the
wedding band she now unconsciously fingered.

"Clete!" Fern murmured as she proffered her
rouged cheek for his kiss. Long jet earrings dangled
from the woman's ears, and an oversized dinner ring
of three black pearls rimmed by large diamonds
glittered on the hand that circled Clete's neck briefly
in an intimate greeting.

"And Mindy!" Fern addressed Clete's wife, standing silently beside him.

Miranda felt she needed all the poise she could
muster as she moved to greet her mother-in-law.

"Elizabeth, how are you feeling today?" Clete's
mother looked rather worn this evening despite the
warm rose of her knee-length cashmere gown.

"I'm fine, my dear, especially now that you're
here. Clete, I'm so glad to see that you're taking
good care of my new daughter-in-law. She looks
every inch the glowing bride."

"You do look cute, little Miranda." Fern joined
the other two women, leaning her long body toward
Clete. "It's easy to see what a temptation you must
have been to Clete. Though it must have been
difficult for a man his age to change his bachelor
ways overnight! He's so used to his freedom, aren't
you, Clete? Have you given up your bachelor apartment?" Fern arched her expressive eyebrows sugges-
tively.

Miranda managed to maintain her cool smile, all
the while wondering how Fern knew about the
apartment where she and Clete had first made love.

Elizabeth took advantage of the break in the conversation to lead her guests into the living room. This evening the velvet draperies were drawn back to give a wide view of the terrace that over-looked the inlet. The sun had all but disappeared behind the horizon, its crimson hue deepening to an intense plum shade. The ice-bound moun-tain range in the far distance stood out vividly, outlined from behind by the disappearing orb of light.

"That's Mt. Redoubt and Mt. Spurr you see from here," Clete told Miranda. "They're volcanoes at the western end of the Alaska Range. Further down Cook Inlet is Mt. Illiamna. All of them are active volcanoes."

"Volcanoes!" Fern exclaimed, appearing at Clete's other side. "How can people live here with all the dangers? Erupting volcanoes, earthquakes, tidal waves, not to mention the wilderness all around you!"

"Clete, would you fix us some drinks before we go in to dinner?" Elizabeth addressed her son.

"What would you ladies like? Mother?"

"I'll have a glass of white wine, thank you."

"Mandy?" Clete turned to his wife.

"I'll have the same as Elizabeth," she murmured.

Fern laughed huskily before he could question her. "You know what I like!" She turned to Miranda and Elizabeth. "Clete makes marvelous Manhat-tans!" Wondering if they would once again be forced to listen to Fern reminisce about the old days with Clete, Miranda sank wearily into the curve of the caned-back sofa.

Clete brought his wife and his mother tall-stemmed crystal goblets filled with golden-hued wine that Miranda found surprisingly good. She noticed that Fern and Clete both drank Manhattans, which she knew were mostly whiskey with a generous dash of vermouth. By the time dinner was announced, Fern had downed three of the potent drinks. Miranda marveled at the woman's capacity for spirits. Even the one glass of wine affected her, she thought, standing up dizzily. She would have tripped if Clete had not taken her arm.

"Wine gone to your head?" he murmured.

"Of course not!" Miranda exclaimed, angry that he thought her such a child.

"Ummm," was Clete's noncommittal reply as he guided her into the elegant dining room without another word.

Clete seated Miranda first, then assisted his mother to her chair at one end of the long table. Then he moved to Fern, pulling out the chair opposite Miranda before he took his place at the head of the elegantly set table. The polished rosewood gleamed in the flickering candlelight, the long tapers set inside hurricane-style columns of glass. A low centerpiece of fresh flowers decorated the center of the table.

"You may say grace, Clete," Elizabeth directed him. Clete bent his dark head and gave a simple but effective benediction that touched Miranda. It was a ritual that had departed from her life along with her mother, but now she realized how much she had missed it.

When Clete raised his head, Joyce appeared to serve the appetizers, beautifully artistic salads crowned with Alaskan King Crab meat cut into bite-sized pieces and a delicious lemon sauce.

The main dish proved to be a succulent standing

rib roast cooked to rare perfection. Joyce placed it beside Clete, who deftly carved the tender meat.

"Oh, the salad was enough for an entire meal!" Fern insisted. "Cut me just a small piece of the roast. I have to watch my figure."

"Miranda?" Clete asked after he had served Fern and Elizabeth. He served her a normal-sized portion of the dish that was perfectly complemented by fluffy whipped potatoes, creamy gravy and a medley of fresh vegetables.

"Oh, you young girls," Fern chastised, "you don't realize how easy it is to let yourselves go! How are you going to appeal to the opposite sex when you lose your girlish figure?" Fern surveyed Miranda with indulgent amusement.

"I suppose a dancer is required to watch her figure more than the average woman," Elizabeth commented.

"Of course," Fern replied.

"And it wouldn't be advisable for a career-oriented dancer to let her body stretch out of shape, say from childbearing," Elizabeth continued slyly.

"Good heavens, no! And thankfully, modern men aren't so insistent on having children."

"I think most men would like children to carry on their family name, though, even in these liberated times. Don't you agree, Clete?" Elizabeth asked innocently.

"Very much, Mother. That's one of the predominant reasons men marry." His mouth twisted in a wry smile, but he did not lift his eyes from his plate. Miranda felt herself flushing. Wasn't that precisely the reason Clete had married her? Not because he loved her, but because he deemed her to be an excellent mother for the children he desired. Perhaps their divergent opinions on the subject of children had come between Fern and Clete. It was obvious they had disagreed.

"Tell me about your career, Fern," Elizabeth prompted, giving Mandy respite from her painful thoughts.

Fern explained that she had been a dancer for a few years before she had been offered small parts in several well-known movies. She rattled off a sizable list of credits, and even Miranda was impressed. However, as she and Elizabeth were both apparently not enthusiastic moviegoers, neither woman could say she had seen one of Fern's performances.

"And is Fern Cassidy your real name or is it a pseudonym? It's quite catchy, I think." Elizabeth asked.

"Oh, no, it's my real name. Cassidy was my first husband's name and I've always liked it." She smiled across the table at Miranda. "Now, take your name, Miranda Montana." Mandy looked up from her plate and gave Fern her full attention.

"Miranda Montana sounds like some hokey Hollywood name, don't you think? It's just the type of name my agent would come up with!" She laughed. "It reminds me of an article I read on the plane coming up here about the crazy names parents give their children. What was your maiden name, Miranda?"

"Bridger," Miranda answered politely.

"Oh," Fern exclaimed. She glanced sharply at Miranda. "Quite an esteemed name in the Wild West! But you're probably not related to the famous oil magnate, George Bridger, are you?"

"He's my father," she said quietly.

Her revelation surprised even Elizabeth who exclaimed in astonishment. "Why, I had no idea, my dear!"

"Well, Clete, it seems you've done rather well for yourself. I congratulate you on your acquisition." Fern lifted her glass. "It would seem you're coming up in the world."

Clete's jaw muscles tightened as he turned to Fern. "I assure you I have no need of the Bridger money, nor do I have the need to elevate my so-called social status," he said coldly.

"Oh, darling, don't be angry!" Fern extended long, plum-tipped fingers and laid them over Clete's left hand which was resting on the polished wood of the table. She rubbed Clete's fingers, caressing the gold and silver wedding band. "I wasn't casting any disparagement on your family background. You have such a wonderful mother, and I love her already!" She dismissed the subject of Elizabeth with a patronizing smile and focused her attention back to Miranda's pale face.

"It must be fabulous to be born with the proverbial silver spoon, growing up so sheltered and pampered; all the best schools, all those lovely clothes and debutante balls. Good heavens, what will happen when you get tied down to the drudgery and hard work of being a mother?"

"But . . ." Miranda had the perverse urge to explain that she, too, had worked for a living, but decided she owed no explanations to this hateful woman.

"Isn't it fortunate that Clete can afford me?" She slanted her husband a dazzling smile, recalling that he too had expressed similar misconceptions of her background earlier in the day. "And how fortunate that I'm so adept at whiling away my time. I suppose

I do spend much of my time in bed these days anyway, don't I, Clete?" Miranda's smile was wicked in implication, but she lowered her lashes discreetly.

Clete did not answer, but Fern gasped audibly. Elizabeth smiled at her daughter-in-law. "That's what honeymoons are for, Mandy!"

Joyce appeared to whisk away the dinner plates. "Would you care for dessert now?" she inquired of no one in particular. By the gleam in her eyes, Miranda could tell she had heard the conversation.

"Well, I can't speak for Miss Cassidy or Mother, but I know that my wife and I would love a piece of that blueberry pie I glimpsed in there." Joyce smiled at Clete and turned to serve coffee and dessert.

"Sanger dropped by today," Elizabeth commented as they left the dining room. "He said you were back to work today. I hope they haven't had any problems." Sanger was Clete's executive assistant, the one who had taken up the reins of the company when Clete had been away.

"Everything is as hectic as usual for this time of year. It's time I came home," Clete answered. He had not resumed his place in the comfortable Louis XV chair. Instead he lounged in the open door to the patio, enjoying the cool night breeze. "Tomorrow Mandy and I need to get some papers settled between us, and then I'll be off to Kobuk."

He turned to Miranda as she uttered a sound of dismay. "I won't be gone any longer than necessary," he explained. "In fact, I'll have Adam drive me to the airport so you can have the Mercedes, in case you and Jane decide to do some more shopping." Miranda stared at Clete, wondering if he was being facetious, but his face betrayed no emotion.

"Well," Fern interrupted, "now that you've made your little bride happy with the prospect of another shopping spree, take me out on the terrace for a breath of fresh air. I need to walk off some of that fabulous dinner!" Fern expertly maneuvered Clete out the door. The two tall figures disappeared into the darkness.

Elizabeth sighed wearily as she sank onto the sofa. Miranda feared she was poor company. Her attention continuously wandered to the couple on the terrace, their voices an indistinct hum in the background.

"I must say you're nothing at all like your father," Elizabeth remarked.

"You know him?" Miranda's attention was effectively caught by Elizabeth's observation.

"We've met. He was up here on business several years back, and I attended a cocktail party given in his honor. He's a dynamic man."

"And ruthless, too," Miranda added. "He'll do anything to get his own way."

"It sounds as if you two don't get along."

"That's the funny part about it, Elizabeth," Miranda mused bitterly. "We'd always gotten along. But I found out in a rather abrupt way that the man I loved and admired never existed except in my own little dream world, a world of illusion that he helped to construct."

A thoughtful silence fell between them. Elizabeth changed the subject. "You look so beautiful in green, Mandy." She smiled, looking at her daughter-in-law with fondness. "And your wedding ring complements it so well. Hud would be so pleased to know that Clete gave it to his wife. You know that Hud carved that ring himself and presented it to my mother on their twenty-fifth wedding anniversary? It means a great deal to our family."

"Clete told me," Miranda replied, "and I feel very proud that he felt he could give it to me. It made our wedding so very special," she replied in a low voice, remembering the touching ceremony.

"Have you told Clete you love him?"

Miranda shook her head. Embarrassed, she looked down at the ring on her finger.

"You don't think he feels the same way?" Elizabeth asked in a very low voice.

"I don't know, Elizabeth," Miranda whispered. "He's never said he loves me." It was painful to admit this to her new mother-in-law.

"Mandy, my son was unmarried for such a long time! You must give him a chance to adjust!"

"I thought we had a chance . . . but now I just don't know." Another thoughtful silence stretched between the two women who were comfortable enough with one another not to feel the necessity of needless chatter.

Elizabeth sighed and stood up. "I hope you'll forgive me, Mandy, but I don't think I could face any more of that woman tonight. I think I'll go to my room for the evening."

"Can I do anything to help?"

"Yes, thank you, dear. You can go to the kitchen and ask Joyce to fix me a cup of hot milk. I'm sure that's just the thing I need to get me to sleep."

Miranda took the hot milk up to Elizabeth's bedroom. She set the small silver tray laden with the fragile cup on the bedside table before bidding her

mother-in-law a fond good night. Quietly she slipped
down the curved staircase that ended in a wide
landing opposite the entrance to the living room.

Clete and Fern were still on the terrace and
Miranda did not feel she had a right to intrude. The
thought angered her. After all, Clete was her husband, and they had not yet been married even two
full days. She clicked off some of the lights in the
living room and sank into the velvet comfort of the
bergère.

She couldn't help hearing Fern's husky voice
speak her name. "Now that I know Miranda's
background, Clete," Fern said, "I understand why
you jumped at the chance to marry her. And she is
attractive in her own way. Even I can see that she
has a certain appeal, at least enough to keep her in
your bed for a while."

"That's enough, Fern!" Clete told her sharply. In
the dimness of the living room, Miranda held her
breath, wondering if Fern and Clete realized how
well their voices carried in the darkness. Clete
continued, "Mandy is my wife now, and our marital
affairs are none of your business!" His voice was
hard.

"But you must know how much I regret throwing
away the chance I had with you, don't you, darling?"
Fern pleaded in a low, sensual voice.

Miranda watched as Clete put his hands on Fern's
tanned arms. "I want you to know that Miranda is
more than just a woman to me, Fern. She's my best
friend, and she will be the mother of my children."

Fern laughed almost triumphantly. "But don't you
see, that suits me just fine, Clete! I'll just wait a little
while longer, and when she starts to thicken around
the waist, I'll be here, waiting with open arms. I

never really wanted to be hampered by a pregnancy, and I certainly don't look the motherly type! Miranda is welcome to have your children who will certainly benefit from their two illustrious family lines! But I'll have what really counts, I'll have you."

"You have it all figured out, don't you?" Clete said. His tone was ironic. Miranda watched helplessly as the other woman pulled Clete's mouth to hers in a clinging kiss.

Mandy bit her lips, afraid to move yet not wanting to hear or see more. He had relegated Miranda to being his "best friend!" And then he had kissed Fern. Miranda's eyes stung as she valiantly fought back the flood of tears that would never stop if once let free. She sat very still, her body as cold as stone while she regained her composure.

Clete and Fern finally came back inside. Clete inquired about his mother and, although it was hard for her to speak, Miranda assured him Elizabeth was most likely fast asleep.

"Well, Miranda," Fern announced after Clete said they must leave, "I hope we'll be seeing more of one another. Perhaps while Clete is out of town, we could get together for lunch." Miranda looked away, murmuring a noncommittal reply. She was relieved when Clete did not linger over their good-byes and ushered her out of Elizabeth's home.

The next morning Clete went to work at a later hour, taking Miranda with him. True to his word, they went to his bank where he made out a request for new checks to be issued in their joint names and he gave her his credit cards to use until a duplicate set arrived. Back at his office, he gave Miranda a tour of the facilities, introducing her to every worker they encountered. It eased her wounded pride to hear him introduce her as "my wife, Mandy," and her low spirits gradually lifted. After their tour, his secretary, Gloria March, fixed them coffee served in Clete's spacious high-rise office. The wide glass window gave a panoramic view of the bustling city spread out below them.

"Anchorage has a mere 200,000 residents, yet that's half the state's population," Clete explained as they stood beside the window. "That's a billion-dollar skyline out there," he added. Pride in his hometown made his deep attractive voice warm. "And the city is still growing. We have all the benefits of a thriving metropolis on the outside, yet we've the advantage of the wilderness just a stone's throw away. A great place to raise a family." He looked down at his wife and smiled. She returned it with a tentative curve of her own lips. Perhaps they had a chance, after all, she thought, looking up at his tall figure. He spoke as if their relationship was a permanent one, yet she could not get out of her mind the picture he and Fern had made on the terrace. On the other hand, he kept mentioning the family he and Miranda would raise here in the land his grandfathers had helped to pioneer. Surely that meant something. Miranda wanted nothing more than to share his future here in this great land, yet she was not sure she could endure life without his love. The last thing she wanted to do was to hold on to Clete Montana just because she was the mother of his child. Her hand went unconsciously to her waist, wondering if there would be a child soon.

Clete accompanied Miranda to the ground level of the building as he explained his itinerary. "I had planned to catch a flight out this afternoon, but I've delayed it to a later one tonight. I have to catch up on a few last minute projects." She must have looked desolate because he laughed sympathetically. "Don't look so mournful. I'll be back in a few days." He drew her to him, ignoring the fact that they stood at the curb of a busy city street. He kissed her long and deep. She was thoroughly flushed when he drew away and opened the rear door of the black limousine. After he seated her, he bent, hesitating for a moment. "Do me a favor, Mandy. Pack me a suitcase and have Adam bring it back. I'm afraid I won't even have time to come home before my flight." She nodded, unable to speak. He pressed another hard kiss on her lips and walked away quickly, not once looking back to wave.

Back at the house on the lake, Miranda fixed Adam a fresh cup of coffee, leaving him in the kitchen to wait while she packed Clete's suitcase. She had not known what type of clothing he would need where he was going north of the Arctic Circle but Adam had proved a great help. As she packed, she followed the chauffeur's instructions. Later, the sight of the chauffeur leaving with Clete's case securely in his hand depressed her, so she threw herself into several cleaning projects, ending up puttering around in the airy modern kitchen when the telephone rang early in the evening.

Thinking it might be Clete, she hurried to answer it.

"Miranda?" Fern's low voice came through the receiver.

"Yes."

"I'm calling to see if you could come into town tomorrow to have lunch with me. We have so much to talk about . . ." Miranda heard a sound in the

background as Fern hesitated. "Excuse me," said
the older woman as she turned to call to someone in
the room with her. "Yes, I'm coming, darling!" Her
voice then turned its attention back to the telephone. "They won't hold the plane just because I'm
dawdling." She gave a throaty chuckle and Miranda
heard a deep masculine voice in the background,
urging Fern again to hurry. Miranda's heart sank. It
took an effort to speak, but Miranda finally managed
to answer Fern's invitation with amazing coolness
and presence of mind.

"I already have plans, Miss Cassidy," she answered politely, the words sticking in her throat,
"but thank you for the thought." As she put down
the receiver, she knew that Fern had not called to
invite her to lunch. She had called at that particular
moment to make sure Miranda would know that she
was with Clete. She was probably one of the "last-
minute projects" he had spoken of earlier in the day.
The tears that Miranda had held in check the night
before flowed freely now, but when they were spent
and she was in Clete's bed, there was no welcome
healing, no respite from the pain. Wide-eyed, she lay
staring in the dark until late into the night.

Chapter Nine

During the next two days, Miranda kept to herself. She found release in intense physical activities, doing yard work, cleaning windows, straightening the shelves in the garage. The physical exertion helped her to fall asleep in her lonely bed, but inevitably she awoke several times during the night to reach for the comfort of Clete's eager embrace before she remembered groggily that he was not there.

She washed and waxed the Mercedes, finding a sense of satisfaction in all her activities. Her favorite, she found, was gardening, and on her third afternoon alone, she was crouched in the soft, rich earth planting some flowering plants that would bring color to the side of the house in late fall. She wore a pair of worn jeans topped by one of Clete's old shirts. Its tails hung practically to her knees and the shoulders drooped over her slender figure. A streak of black ran unnoticed across her forehead where she had reached to push back a piece of stray hair escaping from the knot at the base of her neck.

Miranda glanced up, her attention caught by the flash of a mirror, and she saw with a start the black limousine pulling sedately into the long curving driveway. Adam brought the vehicle to a smooth stop and stepped out to open the rear door. As Miranda stood up to watch, her pulse inexplicably quickened and she expected to see Clete unfold his long legs from the back of the car. But it wasn't Clete, it was Fern Cassidy.

She caught Fern's deprecating glance across the entire expanse of emerald lawn. Mandy smoothed her earth-covered hands on the front of her shirt, an action that served no other purpose than to spread more dirt on the material.

Fern looked resplendent in a casual outfit that was elegantly flamboyant. Very Hollywood, Miranda thought with chagrin as she watched Fern slowly remove her oversized sunglasses. The redhead's flyaway hair was gathered in a chic knot at the top of her head with tendrils of curls framing her carefully made-up face. A braided length of royal blue cloth circled her forehead like the crown of some mystical Greek goddess. On anyone else, the outfit of turquoise, royal blue and poppy colors would look ridiculous, but on Fern it looked the height of fashion. Her dancer's legs were encased in figure-hugging pants of midcalf length, her long, bony feet displayed in backless navy heels. Fern, in turn, observed Miranda with open amusement.

"Goodness!" she exclaimed in greeting. "Don't

you have a gardener, Mandy? What would Clete say if he returned to find his bride looking like a dirty street urchin?" She waved poppy-tipped nails in the air.

"What my husband would say is my problem, not yours, Fern." Miranda said, not caring that she spoke rudely. But her tone of voice did not bother Fern, who lifted the strap of an oversized handbag to her well-formed shoulders.

"I'm sure it's a lovely day to work in the garden," Fern replied. "Why it's almost hot today! Why don't you invite me in for some iced tea?"

"I don't think I'm really dressed for tea in the parlor." Mandy lifted her dirty hands for emphasis.

A movement at her side caught Miranda's attention. Adam stepped forward. "If you wouldn't mind, Mrs. Montana, I'd be honored to serve you ladies on the deck."

"Why, Adam, that would be lovely!" Fern accepted without Miranda's approval.

Miranda raised expressive eyes to Adam and shrugged. The chauffeur returned her glance with a wry one of his own before he turned to go inside. Mandy followed Fern across the verdant grass.

Adam served them tall glasses of iced tea. Miranda smiled her thanks, grateful for something cool to drink.

"I didn't realize gardening was such hard work!" she replied to Fern's pointed gaze as Miranda quickly downed half of the contents of her glass.

"No, I suppose you've always had gardeners to do that for you," Fern replied, her tone pleasantly conversational. "Oh, my dear! Look what you've done to your nails!" She regarded Mandy's broken nails with concern. She reached for the bag that rested on the wooden decking at her feet. "You really should have worn gloves. Here, let me show you how to repair the damage. . . ." Fern reached into her handbag, pulling out several articles as she tried to find the manicure set she finally produced. In returning some of the things she had removed, she reached for a folded section of newspaper she had set aside. "Oh, here's something I found in the morning news. I thought you might appreciate it." Casually Fern pushed the newspaper across the table. She watched Miranda's face intently even as she pretended to be occupied with the manicure set.

Curious at what Fern could find so interesting in a local Anchorage newspaper, Miranda picked it up. The section fell open under her fingers, revealing a picture of a brown-haired girl. The headline beneath read MISSING HEIRESS SOUGHT, and in smaller letters under the heading the article read, "Oil Magnate George Bridger Hospitalized." The girl was Miranda; she recognized the picture as being one she had had taken upon her graduation from college. Miranda's fingers felt wooden. She dropped the paper onto the tabletop.

"It seems there's more to your little story than you and Clete let on," Fern probed.

Miranda looked up in a daze. "What? I'm sorry, I wasn't listening."

"It's nothing important. How ill is your father? I'm afraid I didn't take the time to read the entire article. You see, I've been rather busy moving out of Elizabeth's place."

"You're moving out? You're leaving . . .?"

Fern laughed her trained actress laugh, light and well modulated. "I'm not leaving Alaska as yet, if that's what you were hoping, Miranda! No, things are getting far too interesting to leave just yet. And Clete has generously given me the use of his apartment so I'll be very comfortable while I wait." She stood up, and as Miranda's gaze followed the upward movement, she caught the glittering venom in the woman's eyes. Fern hated her, Miranda realized, and she had come here to deliberately give her the newspaper and to inform her that Clete had installed her in his apartment.

"Clete Montana is mine!" Fern hissed. "I want him back, Miranda Bridger, and I'm this close!" She held up two fingers close together in emphasis. "Surely you've heard that anything goes in love and war. And I feel it only fair to warn you that I always win the battle." With that formidable challenge ringing in her ears, Miranda watched Fern take up her shoulder bag and disappear into the house. A little while later she heard the limousine pull away. Fern had left the newspaper article behind, and Mandy sat down to ponder the headlines for a very long time.

The eye-catching article stated that George Bridger had been seen checking into a hospital in the Houston suburbs, and his daughter, said to be traveling incognito on a backpacking expedition in Alaska's interior bush country, was being sought. Miranda knew that he had developed an irregular heartbeat during his periodic physical the year before. The article did not say whether he was in for tests, and for all she knew he could be dying of a heart attack, could already be dead. Despite the fact that her father had deliberately deceived her, she realized that she still loved him. She buried her head in her arms to rest for a long time while she thought about the two men in her life, her father and her husband. How much alike were these two men?

She sat on the deck for a very long time, until the evening breeze chilled her and forced her indoors. Then she went to the telephone and dialed information. When she reached the hospital that her father had checked into, she asked to speak to George Bridger.

A nurse answered the telephone and after another polite inquiry, Mandy was informed that he could not be disturbed for any reason. It was after eleven o'clock, central time, four hours later than Alaska time. She couldn't get any information at all from the woman, and Miranda knew that this was the way her father operated. There had been the fear of reporters infiltrating or of unscrupulous people calling simply because of his widely touted affluence. When Miranda was a child, her mother had been constantly afraid that someone would kidnap her, the Bridger's only child, and hold her for ransom. Security around all of the Bridgers had always been tight.

On impulse Miranda dialed Dayton's apartment. She wasn't surprised when a woman's voice, husky from sleep, answered. It must be Sandra, she thought wryly, the woman he hadn't wanted to give up, despite the fact that he was marrying someone else. When Day came on the line, Miranda identified herself curtly.

After a short silence over the thousands of miles of intricate cables and satellite connections, Day's sarcastic voice chilled her. "Well, if it isn't the prodigal Bridger child . . . why exactly are you calling?"

"You know very well why I'm calling," she

snapped back. "I saw the article in the paper about Daddy. How is he?"

"As well as can be expected, alone in the hospital with no family at his side for comfort."

"If he hadn't alienated me and my mother with his devious schemes, he'd still have us, or have you come to admire and emulate him so much that you can no longer see objectively, Day?"

There was another long silence at Dayton's end of the connection. It gave Miranda time to gather her thoughts once more after her sudden outburst of anger. How dare he condemn her for leaving!

"What do you mean, devious schemes?" he demanded.

"Oh, Day, haven't you guessed by now that I left because I found out about Charlene and Sandra—that was Sandra who answered your phone . . .?"

"Yes, but what's that got to do with . . . us?"

Miranda interrupted him, angry once more. "It's got everything to do with us, Day. I know about the stocks that you were to receive when you married me. I know how my father kept my mother from seeing me all these years. I also know about Sandra. Do yourself a favor, Day, marry the girl. Maybe you still have a chance to be happy."

Day laughed. "You're jealous, darling Miranda! But nothing has changed by your running away. You'll have to come home eventually, and when you do, you and I will be married as planned. You're not going to ruin all my plans, by heavens!"

As if suddenly realizing the tone of his last statement, his voice softened to the pitch she used to think was so attractive, so appealing. "Miranda, darling, you must know what it's done to me, not knowing where you are, not knowing if you're all right! Your father has been half out of his mind. . . ."

"How is my father?" Miranda cut Day's pleading short.

"It's his heart. Dr. Swanson has been running some tests." Then he hadn't had a heart attack, as she had originally feared, Miranda thought to herself. And Day was hedging. Miranda knew he wasn't going to be pinned down to a definitive answer.

"Tell him I called to let him know I was all right, and I'll check on him again in a few days' time."

"Miranda, wait. . . ." Miranda replaced her telephone receiver in its cradle, not wishing to hear more of Day's lies or pleas.

Padding barefoot into the living room, Miranda switched on the television for some diversion, but she wasn't in the mood for situation comedies or police shows. She switched it off, checked all the doors and windows to see that they were secure and finally retired to her lonely bed.

She tossed and turned for what seemed like hours, and it was well after midnight when she finally fell into a deep slumber. It was a long while later when something brought her slowly to awareness. "Clete . . .?" she murmured, and her low whisper was swallowed up by a firm, demanding mouth over hers. The familiar scent of his cologne was fragrant in her nostrils. Clete had come home to her! She wrapped her arms around his strong neck and spread her fingers downward to feel the rippling muscles under his bare skin.

"You came back!" she exclaimed huskily. Clete whispered in her ear, but her heart and pulses were pounding from the excitement of his nearness. His answering words were lost to her. Her husband had returned, and all Miranda could think of was how much she loved him, how glad she was that she was safely in his arms once more.

Clete's unclad body joined hers, to press her slight form into the soft bed. The sheets tangled as he uncovered her soft skin to his touch. He rained kisses along the sweet curve of her neck, down her creamy shoulders and met the rising swell of her breasts. After savoring them, he continued his explorations, stopping at the curve of her abdomen to kiss the indentation of her navel. His hands made forays to all the places he was eager to rediscover, and Miranda welcomed him. She met his lovemaking with equal abandon, running her hands over his muscled chest, over his hard flat abdomen and down his thighs.

Miranda's senses were at a fever pitch, her mind spinning to envious heights, her body glorying in Clete's touch. Together, they met the rising sun, only to fall asleep in one another's spent arms.

Nestled closely, they slept until early afternoon. Miranda awakened first and gazed down at Clete's arresting face, relaxed in restful slumber. He looked so much like a little boy, his features open and vulnerable, that she felt her heart would surely overflow with love. Not wanting to disturb him, she slipped out of bed, and slipped into her silky champagne gown that had been discarded, forgotten on the floor.

Miranda hummed a happy tune as she fried bacon on the kitchen griddle. She brewed coffee and made toast before breaking open four fresh eggs, cooking them to perfection. Finished, she fixed an elaborate tray and returned to the bedroom.

As she bent over Clete's defenseless features, she

brushed featherlight kisses over his eyes and his hard cheekbones. His lashes fluttered open to reveal the amber eyes she loved so much.

"Breakfast is ready," she whispered.

Pushing back his tousled hair, he sat up, a warm, slumberous smile lighting his features, which were softened by sleep.

"Come join me." He patted a place beside him in the wide bed, propping a pillow on the headboard for her. Side by side, they enjoyed their first meal of the day in companionable silence.

"How was your trip north?" Miranda finally ventured the question. Perhaps he would divulge an innocent reason for Fern's accompanying him to the airport the night he left.

"Very productive," Clete answered as he took a sip of coffee. He was oblivious to her disturbing thoughts. "I brought back volumes of geological surveys and reports that I have to get into a semblance of order. Later in the week I'll collate the results and see if it would be feasible to develop a mine at this new site. I have a feeling we might have come upon a deposit that could significantly add to our country's metal deposits."

Miranda was caught up by the excitement hidden in his words. "What kind of metals did they find?"

"Well, by first estimate, we may have found about eighty million tons of zinc, lead and silver. Out of about thirty-eight holes tested and an estimated 13,000 feet of core drillings, I should be able to come up with a very accurate estimate. When I get that I can go to the board of directors to make the final decision as to whether we should develop the deposit. There are a lot of problems to overcome at this particular site, but I feel good about it. I can't tell you what this might mean to Montana-Hudson, Mandy! You wouldn't possibly understand it all!" But she did understand what Clete was talking about, but now was not the time to tell him of her own geological training and background.

"I'm so glad you had a successful trip." Miranda leaned her head on his shoulder for a quick moment before resuming her breakfast.

"This week will be hectic. I have a thousand things to do, meetings to arrange, but I'll probably be able to wrap it up by early next week, if I'm lucky." She could tell that his mind was already far away, on more important things than his new wife. When he was finished with his bacon and eggs, he moved to get out of bed.

"Do you have to go in today?" Mandy exclaimed in dismay.

"I'm afraid I do." He gazed down at her forlorn face, the expression in his dark brown eyes unfathomable. "I'll tell you what we'll do. I'll leave my surveys here to work on later this evening. I'll make a quick trip to the office and then come home for a quiet dinner, alone with my sexy wife. I'll work on my reports later tonight."

"Well, I guess I'll have to be satisfied with that." Miranda smiled. At least he would not be running to Fern Cassidy on his first night home! She stood to gather up their breakfast things, and Clete went to shower and dress. All too soon, he was driving off in the Mercedes, waving to Miranda who was standing in the open doorway. Memories of their hours alone together touched her mouth with a sensual smile.

* * *

Clete returned home just after seven o'clock, bringing the newspaper in from the delivery box at the end of their long driveway. He tossed it on a kitchen counter and turned to Miranda. He looked tired and withdrawn. Miranda had dinner waiting for him, lobster newberg and a fresh green salad accompanied by a dry white wine.

He threw his suit jacket over a chair, tugged off his tie and sank wearily into his place at the dining room table. The soft candlelight did not disguise the fatigue lines around his eyes, and Miranda's heart went out to him.

He made an effort to inquire about what Miranda had done for the past few days, but she had the nagging feeling that her answers were not really registering in his mind.

After their quiet dinner he excused himself, explaining that he had the geological report on his mind and would retire to his den to tackle the volumes of figures he had mentioned earlier in the day.

"I'll bring you some coffee later," she volunteered.

"Fine." Clete nodded and left her to clean up the dining room and kitchen. Later, when she took the coffee in on a tray, he was deeply engrossed in his work.

Miranda tiptoed behind Clete's chair to place the tray at one side of his massive mahogany desk littered with papers filled with geological data. She could not resist taking a quick glance at the type of reports and was not surprised to find she easily understood their import. She had worked one summer on a work-study project in Colorado and had done similar studies, although not on such an extensive scale. But she resisted saying anything to Clete, not wishing to disturb his concentration.

Instead she silently poured him a cup of the strong coffee and placed it at a strategic spot on his desk top. Clete murmured an absent-minded thanks, briefly touching her hand as she drew it away. Then he was once more engrossed in his studies.

Happy that Clete was in the house, Miranda hummed softly to herself as she entered the bathroom to fill the tub and to add a lavish amount of fragrant bath oil. She spent a languorous hour soaking, her mind wandering to their early morning lovemaking. Clete was ever on her mind.

When she was finished with her bath, she dressed in a long, low-cut nightgown with a matching peignoir, its silver color enhancing the gray of her eyes. Then she wandered down the hallway to watch television or perhaps to read the evening paper. The telephone rang once but she assumed Clete took the call. She heard his deep voice as he spoke to whomever had called.

"No, I'm sorry I didn't have more time this afternoon. Yes, I know I forgot it." He chuckled warmly.

"Well, bring it by my office in the morning, and we'll talk about it." Surmising that he was speaking to one of his co-workers, Miranda turned back, not wanting to disturb his conversation.

Miranda sat down to enjoy a highly entertaining special on television and when it was over, she discovered it was almost midnight, yet she was not at all sleepy.

She was drawn toward Clete's study, wondering if he was still working. She stood by the open door, her slender frame outlined by the light from the hallway. "Are you about finished for tonight?" she asked softly.

Clete rubbed his hands over his face, as if the action could erase the tired lines from around his eyes. He shook his head.

Miranda slipped into the room and came to stand behind him. Her hands kneaded his tired shoulders with the muscles knotted from tension and fatigue. "Clete, if you'd lie down for a few minutes' sleep, I'll wake you up. You won't accomplish much being this tired."

"You're right," he agreed, surprising her. "This morning was the only sleep I've had in forty-eight hours." He stood up, towering over her and walked slowly to the leather couch across the room, flinging himself down with a heavy sigh. Miranda slipped out of the room, but returned quickly with a light quilt and a pillow that she slid under his head. He opened a sleepy eye in acknowledgment and a smile curved his lips as he drifted off to sleep. After Miranda tucked the quilt around his figure, her hand lingered on his shoulder for a moment.

Then she glanced at the digital clock on his desk to check the time. Again her eyes were drawn to the surveys on his desk. His own report summarizing the results rested where he had left it, and she was unable to resist sitting down to peruse his work. She began to read and was completely absorbed in seconds, her analytical mind quickly picking up the threads of Clete's report. He was about three-quarters through his summary and she looked through the remaining reports to see if he would be able to support the conclusions he was obviously leading up to. In a moment her hand grasped a pencil and she was caught up in the technical intricacies of the scientific data. The pencil made light scratching noises as it flew over the paper. Clete's deep breathing provided a soothing background in the quiet room. When Miranda finished her own conclusions, which she had written on scratch paper, she moved to a wide comfortable chair while she proofread her notes. Then, with a tired flourish, she rewrote her conclusions and let the papers rest in her lap. She closed her eyes for a brief moment's rest.

When she woke up she wondered what had disturbed her catnap. She was surprised to find the weak light of dawn filtering in through the draperies. Clete stood in front of her holding her notes in his hands. When he finished reading them, which he did quickly and efficiently, he stared at his wife in open amazement. "You did this." It was more of a statement than a question.

She nodded sleepily as she sat up to ease the crick in her neck. "You were sleeping so peacefully that I hated to disturb you," she told him. He whirled away from her and went to his desk to sit down. He laid her papers next to his.

"The technical data more than supports my recommendation to develop the site," he mused in an excited voice. He started to gather up various sheets of paper, stapling them together in the order he wished. He worked silently, quickly. He added her conclusions to the stack he had worked on. Then he looked up, an inscrutable look falling over his face as he stared across the room at her. He shook his head before glancing at the clock.

"I have to get this to the office, but I need to talk

to you, Miranda. You realize that this," he indicated the completed report, "changes everything. I had no idea you were trained to be anything other than a . . ."

"A social butterfly?" she finished for him.

A wry smile spread over his face. "You really had me fooled." Before she could answer, he strode from the room, picking up a light jacket and his car keys and muttering something about showering and changing in town.

Miranda's first coherent thought was that she needed a cup of strong coffee. Last night's newspaper lay on the kitchen counter, forgotten until now. While the coffee maker gurgled, she idly opened the paper, only to come face to face with a handsome picture of her father. The headlines jumped out at her.

OIL MAGNATE SERIOUSLY ILL. Gathering her wits, she read that George Bridger had checked into the hospital complaining of chest pains and was reported to be in intensive care. The hospital would not confirm his condition, but an unidentified source stated that his condition was "grave." The paper shook in Miranda's trembling hands. Was that what Dayton had been trying to tell her when she had hung up on him, not giving him a chance to finish their conversation?

She ran to the telephone to dial his office number. His secretary was uncooperative, merely telling her that Dayton was at the hospital and would in all probability not be in the entire day. George Bridger must indeed be ill if Dayton missed a day at the office! Miranda felt a terrible dread settle over her.

Hurriedly, she dialed the airlines and booked a

seat on the noon plane. Then she rushed to pack and dress, changing into the same white designer suit she had worn on her flight north. When she was dressed she called a taxi, pacing back and forth until its arrival. She gave the man the address of Hudson-Montana, for she just had enough time to tell Clete where she was going.

The taxi waited while Miranda swiftly found her way to Clete's office on the top floor of the Hudson Building. She remembered the way, but when she entered the anteroom used by his secretary the woman was not there. Clete's door was open, though, and she moved toward it.

"Here's a clean shirt." It was unmistakably Fern Cassidy's voice. "I'll send over the rest of the stuff later with Adam."

"Thanks, Fern," Clete said. "I hope its not in your way. You're quite comfortable in the apartment?"

"Oh, it's fine for temporary measures and I managed to get out some while you were gone."

"Oh?"

"Yes, I visited your little bride. Did you know that I found her knee deep in garden mud, her nails all broken, no makeup on! If I hadn't known better, I'd have sworn she was enjoying herself!"

"That just goes to show you that you don't know Miranda very well." Miranda's heart stopped as she listened to them discussing her so analytically. She wanted to turn around and flee, but something was holding her firmly in place.

"Oh, and I suppose you do?" Fern threw back at him, her voice full of sarcasm. "A spoiled brat that you married on the rebound!"

Clete laughed. "That spoiled brat happens to be a

highly trained, competent geologist," he retaliated. "To get to the level that she is, she must have worked and studied for years."

"Well, well, well . . . that changes everything, doesn't it?"

"Yes, the same thought occurred to me when I found out," Clete murmured thoughtfully.

"Why, if she's as good as you say, she wouldn't have to depend on a husband or even her father for a living, would she?" Fern's voice was full of excitement.

"No, and from everything I've learned about Miranda Bridger in the short time I've known her, I can assure you that she's a woman who is fully able to take care of herself."

"Oh, Clete, that would solve all of our problems! Don't you see?" There was a long silence, but Miranda turned and fled, not wanting to hear her sentence come from Clete himself. He had referred to her so clinically, calling her Miranda Bridger, not Mandy Montana, his wife. She must have been a problem to him while he had been under the impression that she was a woman who must depend fully on a man for her livelihood. But now that he knew she was a trained and capable scientist in her own right, he no longer had to feel any responsibility for her. It seemed that he and Fern had settled their differences and wanted to be together again.

Wild thoughts flew through her mind as she found herself back in the taxi. "International Airport," she told the driver in a remote tone of voice. Her flight from Houston had been impetuous, adventurous, but her flight from Alaska and the Montana family was full of numbing misery. The first time, she had run away on her own accord, of her own free will, but now she was being driven away with the knowledge that her husband had found a way out of their short-lived marriage.

As she sat through the flight from Anchorage to Seattle, she wondered at the passion Clete had always displayed toward her. Then she realized that men were different than women; they obviously could be attracted to one woman while still loving another. Clete had been undeniably attracted to Miranda when he had found himself sharing a wilderness cabin with a pleasing young woman who had made it plain that *she* was attracted to him.

Clete was a sensual, virile man who would never aspire to a celibate existence and had taken advantage of the situation. Of course, he had been completely honest about his intentions toward Miranda, so she shouldn't be complaining. It hadn't been Clete's fault that events had taken such an unexpected turn. He could have had no idea that Fern would simply walk back into his life like she had.

The plane flew steadily southward and passed over the Rockies without Miranda ever taking notice. Her thoughts were of Clete.

Despite everything that had occurred, Miranda knew that Clete was a man who took commitments seriously. He had made a long-term commitment to Miranda, whom he had thought to be a woman used to an idle, useless life, a woman unable to take care of herself. He had been prepared to endure a married life with a woman he did not love. But now that he knew she was quite capable of earning her own living, he could leave her honorably. He could soon marry the woman he loved.

And where would that leave Miranda? She had

been secretly wondering for the past few days whether she might be pregnant. More than ever she hoped she was, for if she could not have Clete, at least she could have his child. She hugged this soothing thought to herself, saving it for future comfort.

By the time the plane touched ground in Houston, it was very late at night. Miranda was mentally and physically exhausted and, realizing she was too tired to make her apartment habitable, she checked into a hotel near the hospital where her father was a patient. Leaving a wake-up call request with the desk, Miranda fell into the deep slumber of the exhausted.

Walking down the long hospital corridor the next morning, Miranda's thoughts were composed. Outwardly, she appeared calm. She had prepared herself for the worst, and now she thrust all thoughts of Clete and her future out of her mind. At the moment her father deserved her consideration. She was sure that her father would be in intensive care, but this was not the surgical floor, nor did it seem to be the coronary care section. She looked for the room number, and when she came to the designated doorway, she saw it was a sumptuous private room. She caught sight of several lavish bouquets of flowers, and as she stepped closer she saw a woman packing a suitcase opened across the bed.

"Is that everything?" the woman asked someone out of Miranda's line of vision.

"Yes, just the flowers," said a man, his voice uncharacteristically mellow as he spoke to the woman. Slim and well dressed, the gray-haired lady threw a loving glance in the direction of the voice.

"I'll get those and call for the car," Dayton

Green's voice volunteered. At the very moment she recognized her former fiancé's voice, her father strode into view, his figure as tall and as strong as it had ever been.

"Miranda!" he exclaimed sharply.

Dayton was instantly at her father's side. In a moment, Miranda found herself drawn into the room.

"But, Daddy, the papers said you were ill!"

George and Day laughed. The woman looked serious. She threw a worried glance to a far corner of the room where a beautiful blond woman was seated, her blue eyes quickly hiding a flash of resentment that Miranda caught just before she lowered her lashes.

"Well, I'm glad to see that you still think enough of me to rush to my side." George seemed pleased. "I guess your little plan worked, Day. You know my little girl better than I do!" He turned to the older woman who was still standing in front of the suitcase. "Pack this, too, will you? I haven't finished reading it." He threw a financial magazine down on top of the open case. Then he turned toward his daughter.

"What little plan?" Miranda demanded, pulling herself to her full height. She was more self-assured than before, more able to stand up for her rights than the old Miranda, Miranda Bridger, had been. Now she was Miranda Montana, a married woman who could take care of herself and of a child if necessary. She faced her father squarely.

Day answered for him. "When I found out you were in the Anchorage area, I planted that first article in the paper, and sure enough, it got your attention. But you didn't respond, so I had the second article planted. And here you are," Dayton declared as his eyes roved blatantly over her curved figure to rest for a brief moment on the full swell of her breasts before going on to peruse her brown cloud of hair.

"You're telling me that you're not sick." She ignored Dayton and spoke directly to her father. "Then why are you here?"

"I'm just in for my routine checkup," George finally answered his daughter, dismissing the subject with casual disregard. "But I'm glad to see you've come to your senses and decided to come back."

Miranda could not believe what she was hearing. For a frantic moment, her glance went to the woman in front of the suitcase. The woman's lips twisted in resignation and she shrugged. She was apparently used to the scheming of these two men.

"You look fantastic, Miranda!" Day stepped close to her, but Miranda stepped away. "Now that you're back, we can get new invitations printed up. I don't want to wait as long as before. I think we can do with a smaller wedding than we had planned. It will be more meaningful and . . ."

"It's too late, Day," Miranda interrupted.

"You're back now, and I understand. Every bride has a moment when she feels hesitant."

"No, you're wrong about that. If it's the right man, the bride wouldn't be hesitant." She knew that, she spoke from experience.

"Now, Miranda," George intervened. "Day told me why you ran away, and I can explain all about your mother and the stocks, which, by the way, are for both of you, but Dayton is much better qualified to handle your affairs. It was all for your own good."

"Was threatening my mother's husband for my

own good, too?" she asked. Her head was clear now. "And was hiding Charlene's existence all for my own good? I might have learned to love her." She whirled around to Day. "And Sandra, how do you think she feels to be put in second place to a wife you want only so you can get ahead, second place even to a pile of stocks you want so badly that you'd ruin three lives, yours, mine, and Sandra's?" Miranda glanced across the room. Briefly the shuttered eyes stared at Miranda.

"But I love you, Miranda . . ." Day insisted. Sandra did not attempt to hide the pain in her shimmering blue eyes.

"Don't lie to me! I've heard it all before, and it doesn't mean a thing to me! I'm leaving, and this time I won't come back!" Miranda whirled on her heels.

"If you leave, Miranda Bridger, you'll never get a penny of your inheritance from me, now or after I'm dead and gone." George Bridger said coldly.

"That suits me just fine, and the name is not Miranda Bridger, it's Miranda Montana!"

"Why you lying little—!" Dayton exclaimed hoarsely, grabbing her arm cruelly. "You were leading me on and all that time you had someone else on the side! And I thought you were a scared little virgin who was saving herself for her wedding night!" Day's face was livid with fury. "I won't let you get away with ruining all my plans!"

"But I have ruined all your plans, Day," Miranda replied quietly. "I am married now." Her gray eyes met his with icy steadiness. After a long moment, his grasp loosened and fell away.

"As I advised you the other night, Day, the best thing you could do is to find your own happiness.

And I don't think you have to look very far to find it." She threw a quick glance in Sandra's direction. "As for you, Dad, I think it's far too late for you to make amends, not to mention changing your despotic ways. But I won't be there for you to manipulate, you'll have to find someone else for that!" Charlene's face blanched and Miranda threw her an apologetic glance. "And for whatever it's worth, I'm going to find my mother and beg her forgiveness for ever listening to your cruel lies!" Then Miranda turned her back on the two men who had affected her life so significantly.

Chapter Ten

Miranda wasted no time in checking out of her hotel room. By the time she called a bellhop to carry her bag, the rental car she had requested was waiting outside. She had known for years where her mother lived, and merging into the flow of the heavy daytime traffic, she quickly turned south toward the coastal city of Galveston. A scant hour later, she pulled up to the beachside home of Mr. and Mrs. Miles Hall. Barbara herself answered the doorbell, and when she saw her daughter standing before her, she stood as if in shock for a long moment.

Then Miranda was in her mother's welcoming embrace, and tears clouded the vision of both women. They laughed and cried at the same time. Miranda clung to her mother for a long time.

Several hours later on a palm-shaded patio overlooking the Gulf of Mexico, Miranda asked, "Can you ever forgive me for not believing in you, Mother?"

"Someday when you have children of your own, my dear, you'll find that it isn't so difficult to forgive them. And I know your father much too well to ever put the blame on you, Mandy." Barbara smiled sadly. "I have carried my own share of guilt over the years."

They both thought of the threat George Bridger held over Miles Hall. "What could be so terrible that Dad could blackmail Miles? I wasn't aware that they even knew one another." She looked at her mother's face, beautiful despite the lines around her eyes and the gray streaked liberally through her hair.

"Oh, George and I knew Miles and his first wife many years ago. And yes," she said when she saw the question in Miranda's face, "Miles and I were attracted to one another even then, despite the fact that we were both married to other people. But we fought our feelings, never even speaking of what was in our hearts. You see, Miles's father-in-law was an accountant for Texbridge and he was caught embezzling money from the company." Miranda breathed in sharply. Barbara nodded. "He went to prison, and shortly after that Miles's first wife committed suicide."

"Oh, no!" Miranda exclaimed, sympathy for Miles suffusing her.

"It was a terrible time for Miles, and the only time I saw him in all the years preceding my divorce from your father was at his wife's funeral. For some strange reason George went with me, and I suppose when he saw Miles and me together, he guessed that we loved one another. But it wasn't until I found out about your father's involvement with another woman and told him I wanted a divorce that George came to me with that damnable evidence! If it was taken the wrong way it could have implicated Miles and his wife as having been in on the embezzlement."

Miranda's face tightened as she thought again of how cruel and harsh her father could be.

Barbara continued. "I knew, of course, that Miles would never have done such a thing, and I've never told him of the evidence George showed me that day. He's too honorable a man and would never have stood meekly aside while George blackmailed me to prevent my seeing you. Miles knows how much I love you. He would have faced George in court, but knowing your father as I do, I know Miles might have ended up in prison for years despite the fact that I knew the evidence was pure fabrication."

Just a few short months ago, Miranda would have defended her father against anyone, but now she knew with a certainty that Barbara had always been right. George Bridger was a hard, cruel man who cared only for himself.

"But you stood up to your father alone, Mandy," Barbara marveled. "Clete Montana must be a very special man to arouse such intense feelings. Are you sure he doesn't love you?"

"Oh, Clete likes me very much, mother, but liking is not loving. And I love him enough to want his happiness, even if it lies in being with another woman." Miranda spoke sadly. Barbara nodded in agreement, liking the woman her little girl had become.

"Are you going to go back to tell him you'll give him his freedom? You owe it to him, Mandy."

"I know." she sighed. "But I can hardly stand the

thought of having to see him with another woman, Mother! It would tear me apart." Her gray eyes shimmered silver with unshed tears. "It *has* torn me apart," she amended, the memory of Fern in Clete's arms torturing her.

Barbara teased her daughter lovingly. "You've just stood up to the mighty George Bridger, and you're afraid to face the man you love?"

Miranda smiled back at her mother. "Silly, isn't it?" Then she grew sober once more as her thoughts drifted to Clete and all the things they might have had together. Yet she wondered how long she could have lived with him knowing that he loved someone else. It would have become unbearable and Miranda knew that the love a woman had for her children could never compensate for the lack of love from the man she wanted with all her heart.

"It's better this way, Mother," she said finally, rousing herself from her thoughts. "But you're right, I'll never be able to live with myself if I don't face Clete, just as I feel better for having faced Daddy, despite the fact that it was painful. I'll return to Alaska and give Clete his freedom, with my blessing." Her voice was low with suppressed emotion.

It was raining when Miranda stepped off the plane in Anchorage. The clouds hung low, obscuring the green mountains from view. It was midafternoon and she realized Clete would probably be at his office. When she arrived at the Hudson Building, she carried her suitcase up to her husband's office, and her heart pounded crazily in anticipation.

Mrs. March looked up from her desk in surprise. "But Mrs. Montana your husband left Anchorage yesterday!"

"I've been out of town, my father was very ill . . . and I've just gotten back." She tried to give a plausible reason for her ignorance of Clete's whereabouts.

"Well, that explains it! He probably tried to call you, but couldn't get through. Mr. Montana has taken a leave of absence and caught the first plane to Las Vegas. You probably passed one another in the air!"

Las Vegas! Why would he have gone to Las Vegas—except for a divorce! Had he taken Fern with him, so they would not have to be parted for the months it would take to dissolve his marriage to Miranda? But she couldn't possibly ask Mrs. March if the Cassidy woman had been booked on the same flight out.

"Are you all right, Mrs. Montana? You look very pale."

"Yes, yes, I'm fine. Just disappointed that I missed my husband, that's all. It's been a very hectic three days," Miranda attempted to explain.

"Is . . . is your father going to be all right?" the secretary inquired solicitously.

"Oh, yes, Mrs. March, my father is going to be just fine. There's not much that gets him down for long," she said with unconscious bitterness. "Could you do me a favor, please? Call Adam for me. I think I'll go to my mother-in-law until I hear from my husband."

"Clete left with Fern, didn't he?" Miranda greeted Elizabeth less than an hour later. Her mother-in-law nodded.

"Just yesterday," she verified. "I've never seen Clete look like that. He said that you had returned to

Houston, and that he and Fern were leaving for Las Vegas within the hour. Adam drove them both to the airport." So Adam knew about Clete and Fern, Miranda thought, remembering the sympathetic look the chauffeur had given her. But how had Clete known she had gone back to Houston? She sighed and supposed that he had seen the article in the paper, naturally assuming she would rush to her father's sickbed. But why had he taken such advantage of her absence so quickly? He and Fern must be in a great hurry to be married. But still the facts did not quite fit.

"Didn't he wonder about my sudden departure, Elizabeth?"

The older woman hesitated. "Well, he did say he had received a telephone call from Houston." Miranda's heart stopped as she listened. "A man named Dayton Green called and said that you and he had reconciled your differences. He said you had had a lover's quarrel before you left Houston last month, but now everything had changed." There was that statement again, Miranda thought wildly, everything certainly had changed! Slow fury built up inside her to combine with the inevitable feeling of loss. She realized that somewhere deep inside of her, she had returned to Alaska with the weak hope, but a hope nonetheless, that when she confronted Clete, he would have miraculously decided that he loved Miranda and not Fern. She had hoped he would have discovered that he missed Miranda and loved her. But between Fern and Dayton, that hope had been effectively destroyed.

"When exactly did Dayton call?"

"Why, just yesterday, Mandy," Elizabeth said.

"Clete called the airport from my telephone, that was how eager he was to leave. I'm so sorry, my dear. I'd do anything to change things, but I can't."

"I know you can't, Elizabeth, and I'd be the last person to want Clete to stay with me just for the sake of his family." Miranda laid her head on Elizabeth's comforting shoulder for a moment. "I'll be all right." Then she straightened up, realizing grimly that Dayton had gotten back at her for doing him out of his share in Texbridge. He had called Clete and lied about their relationship. How he must hate her to do such a vile thing!

"Sit down, my dear," Elizabeth instructed her, leading Miranda to the sofa. "Joyce, bring us some tea with a healthy shot of brandy in each cup, please. I think we both need something fortifying."

As they sipped the bracing liquid, the two women talked. Miranda explained how she had found her mother and told Elizabeth how happy Barbara was with Miles.

"What are you going to do now?" Elizabeth inquired.

"I hadn't really thought that far ahead," Mandy admitted. "My mother has offered me a home and, of course, I could always find a good job anywhere there is oil."

"But you don't want to."

"No." Mandy smiled ruefully. "All I wanted was Clete and our family. Now nothing else seems to matter." She set her cup down.

"What you need is a breathing space, time to adjust to a different way of life, my dear. You need time to think things through before you come to a final decision. And I think I have just the solution."

She patted Miranda's cold hand. "Just leave everything to me. But right now, it's time for you to get
some rest. It's late."

After Miranda had placed a short call to Barbara
and Miles to let them know she had arrived safely,
she allowed Joyce to show her to a guest room, and
later the woman appeared with a tray laden with
homemade soup and light rolls. After the satisfying
meal, Miranda sank into the thankful oblivion of
sleep.

The next morning, Miranda was dismayed to learn
that her mother-in-law wanted her to fly out to
Clete's cabin on the remote lake in the Talkeetna
Mountains. But no matter what objections Miranda
could come up with, Elizabeth would have it no
other way. Miranda needed some time to gather her
thoughts and to get herself on the right track once
again. She had to live her life, even if it wasn't the
life she had dreamed about. The cabin would be just
such a place, Elizabeth had insisted.

Elizabeth had sent Joyce to Clete's home to pack
suitable clothing for Miranda's trip, articles that
would be appropriate for the bush country. After a
quick farewell to Elizabeth and Joyce, Miranda was
driven by Adam to Lake Hood where a floatplane
had been chartered to fly her to the lake.

Hours later Miranda was standing on the shore of
the familiar lake, waving good-bye to the pilot, who
was scheduled to return in a week's time to pick her
up for the return flight to Anchorage. Miranda
watched the small plane disappear over a mountain,
the sound of its engine lingering long after the plane
had gone from sight. Then she turned to enter
Clete's mountain cabin, alone.

* * *

The week passed slowly and time hung heavily on Miranda's hands. Memories crowded her mind. She did not venture far from the cabin because the pilot of the charter plane had reinforced her healthy fear of bears, who were not yet in hibernation. Adam had packed an ample supply of foodstuffs for her, and there was plenty of water and wood for one person.

During the day she stayed outside for long hours, hiking around the perimeter of the lake for much-needed exercise. One afternoon her attention was caught by the haunting noise of wild geese flying south in a ragged vee formation. Winter would come soon to this wild northland, and they were escaping the cold climate while they could.

Long quiet days followed dream-tossed nights until it was soon time for the return of the charter plane. Early on her sixth day in the wilderness, she heard the drone of an engine. As she was preparing her primitive flower bed for its winter sojourn, she caught sight of the craft dipping down to circle the lake once, then the floats touched water and skimmed over the blue surface. The plane was a day early, she thought.

Soon she saw the pilot jump onto the dock to secure the floatplane. When he straightened up from his task, Miranda's heart stopped. It was Clete. Wiping her hands clean, she moved toward the lake on wooden legs and willed herself to be calm.

Clete walked toward Miranda where she waited at the end of the long rustic pier. He had never looked as handsome as he did in the rough outdoor clothing, his gray and blue checked wool shirt drawn tightly across his familiar broad shoulders, his faded denims taut over narrow, masculine hips. His amber eyes sought Miranda's face.

"Thank heavens my mother had the foresight not to let you leave the state before I had a chance to get back!" Clete exclaimed in his deep voice.

Miranda panicked. Did Clete mean he was coming back to her just because his mother wanted him to? She turned to run, afraid she would not be able to resist him if that was the case.

"Oh, no, you don't!" Clete exclaimed, running after her. She outdistanced him for a short time but his longer strides caught up with hers. He reached out to grab her arm, but she resisted, sending them toppling together into a spongy bed of green moss.

"You're not going to run away from me any more," he panted, his hand still grasping her slender wrist. "I want you, Miranda, I always have."

"Want is not love!" she cried defiantly, rolling away from him, and coming to a sitting position several feet away.

"And who says that I don't love you?"

Miranda's heart skipped several radical beats before her spirits sank to their previous low. "Don't, Clete. I can't live a lie anymore." Her voice was very low but he heard her. He sat up, too, his figure suddenly rigid as he waited for her to explain. "A marriage can't survive on just the love of one person," she said. "It takes two to make it work the way it should." Her voice sounded strangled to her own ears, but she had to speak the truth. She didn't want him when his heart belonged to someone else.

"I suppose you're right." He sighed deeply, his shoulders slumping. "I guess Mother was mistaken." He looked out over the lake, a remote look settling over his strong features. "She had given me hope that we could work things out."

"It'll be better this way, Clete, you'll see." Her hand went out to touch his, lying limply on the velvety green moss. He jerked away from her. Hurt, she continued, "We'll get a quick, civilized divorce and then you can marry the woman you always wanted."

"You mean you can marry the man you always wanted." Bitterness suffused his words.

"No, I gave up my chance for love," she whispered.

"Do you mean to tell me that Dayton Green is throwing you over now that you've gone back to him? That vindictive son of a . . ." Now Clete was angry. "I'm sorry, Mandy, I just wanted you to be happy." He moved toward her, but it was her turn to rebuff his sympathy. Confused by their conversation, she stood up and walked to the edge of the lake.

"And you know I wish you and Fern all the best, Clete." The words almost choked her, but they had to be said. She truly wanted the best for the only man she would ever love. Tears filled her eyes and she turned away quickly before he could see them.

"Fern? What the devil does that woman have to do with anything?" he demanded almost angrily, jumping to his feet.

"Well . . . didn't you go with her to Las Vegas?" Miranda turned to look at Clete in confusion.

"We took the same plane out, but only because I wanted to make certain she was out of my life once and for all!"

"You didn't file for a divorce in Las Vegas?" He shook his head.

"Where did you go, then?" she asked.

A strange look came over Clete's face and he took one hesitant step toward Miranda. "I went to Houston, hoping to find you. But you had already been and gone. Neither your father nor Dayton Green would tell me anything. You led me on a merry chase! I finally figured out on my own that you went to your mother's, but by the time I found out her married name and got in contact with her, Barbara told me I was too late."

"Did she tell you anything about . . . my plans?"

"No, she said it was your prerogative to tell me how you feel, not hers. And Elizabeth said almost the very same thing when I followed you back to Anchorage." A slow smile curved his lips. "Just why did you come back to Alaska?" he asked as a sudden light came to his eyes. "Aren't you going to tell me?" He stepped even nearer until they were standing so close that they could touch. But they did not, each afraid to make the first tentative move.

"I . . . can't." Miranda looked down at the shore beneath her feet. She couldn't take the chance that he would take pity on her and pretend to love her just because she admitted she really loved him.

"Look at me, Miranda," he demanded. Reluctantly, she obeyed, raising her eyes to meet his.

"Miranda Montana," her husband told her, "I love you, with all my heart and soul, I love you!"

A strange weakness suffused her body, and if Clete hadn't reached out to gather her into his arms, she would surely have fallen. She buried her face in the front of his woolen shirt that was fragrant with the scent of his aftershave lotion. Her hands were pressed flat against Clete's chest, and she could feel the strong beat of his heart beneath her fingers.

Slowly she moved her hands upward until they circled his neck. Then she raised her eyes that glowed with a happiness she had thought she would never again experience.

"I hope this isn't a dream, Clete Montana," she whispered. "I've waited so long to hear those words from your lips that I'm afraid I'm hallucinating."

His voice was low, intense with feelings that matched her own. "And why did you want to hear those particular words, Mandy, my love?"

"Because I love you, Clete. I've loved you since the first time you carried me over the threshold of your home scarcely thirty minutes after we first met. . . ."

Clete bent, picking her up in his strong arms just as he had so long ago, his mouth covering hers even as he strode toward the cabin. He carried her over its rustic threshold and unhesitatingly went to his bedroom. Gently he settled her on the soft mattress. As he joined her, his hands came up to frame her delicate face, which was flushed from his heady kisses.

"I've been such a fool, Miranda, not to have admitted it sooner, to you and to myself. I can only say that I was blinded by the wild attraction between us. I confused love with desire, but with you, they're one and the same." He gazed down at her, his eyes devouring her as surely as his lips had moments earlier. "Why did you run away without a word? I would have understood about wanting to see Dayton and your father again. I would even have gone with you, to be at your side if you needed me."

"I did come to your office just before I left for the airport!"

"Oh?" Clete frowned in bewilderment.

"You were talking to Fern and I overheard what you said. She was staying at your apartment, and she had brought you a shirt! I thought—"

"Mandy, my darling!" his voice chastised her gently. "I only let her stay in my apartment as a courtesy, for old times' sake. No matter what she had told you to the contrary," Clete paused to kiss Miranda briefly on the nose, "I had only stopped by to pick up my clothes. When she dropped in on me at the office, she was bringing a shirt that I had stupidly left behind—"

"But I heard her tell you how she had visited me and how I was a spoiled brat—" By Clete's grin, Miranda knew that she must sound somewhat childish, but she could not restrain her anxious, jealous thoughts from spilling out. "Then I heard you tell her how I was able to take care of myself, and she said that solved all your problems. . . ."

Clete gathered Miranda in his arms. "You obviously didn't stay to hear the end of the conversation," he murmured. "I told her that she and I didn't have any problems, because there wasn't any 'she and I,' not together anyway. She was just assuming I would eventually succumb to her charms, but I had no intention of losing you, my wife. Fern had always wanted to make our relationship into something more than it was, but I was no more interested in marrying her now than I had been years ago."

"But Fern had led your mother to believe the two of you were on the way to your wedding—" Miranda still sounded doubtful.

Clete laughed but explained tenderly, "I knew nothing about that until later. Only when Adam met me at the airport with the news of the reception did I have any idea that Fern had been so determined! I thought I was angry then, but when the woman showed up on our wedding night implying she might be pregnant, I had to force myself to remain calm. In the first place, we hadn't been intimate—she knew I never loved her—and second, she was intruding on my honeymoon," he concluded.

"Love does strange things to people." Miranda could excuse Fern now that she was certain of Clete's love.

He laughed in agreement. "I can relate to that—I was jealous of Derek for no reason, then I began to wonder if you had married me just to get someone to take care of you after your father's money ran out. That's when I began to realize I wanted so much more from you than that!" He shook his head at his own doubts before nuzzling his face in the warm curve of Miranda's neck. His hands moved to follow the familiar contours of his wife's form. "I've missed you so much!"

His mouth found Miranda's eagerly, and just before she gave herself up to her husband's love-making, she whispered, "Say it again, Clete. . . ."

"That I love you, my Mandy?" She nodded and his words were a gentle whisper in her ear. "I love you, I'm lost in love. . . ."

$1.75 each

- [ ] 157 Vitek
- [ ] 158 Reynolds
- [ ] 159 Tracy
- [ ] 160 Hampson
- [ ] 161 Trent
- [ ] 162 Ashby
- [ ] 163 Roberts
- [ ] 164 Browning
- [ ] 165 Young
- [ ] 166 Wisdom
- [ ] 167 Hunter
- [ ] 168 Carr
- [ ] 169 Scott

- [ ] 170 Ripy
- [ ] 171 Hill
- [ ] 172 Browning
- [ ] 173 Camp
- [ ] 174 Sinclair
- [ ] 175 Jarrett
- [ ] 176 Vitek
- [ ] 177 Dailey
- [ ] 178 Hampson
- [ ] 179 Beckman
- [ ] 180 Roberts
- [ ] 181 Terrill
- [ ] 182 Clay

- [ ] 183 Stanley
- [ ] 184 Hardy
- [ ] 185 Hampson
- [ ] 186 Howard
- [ ] 187 Scott
- [ ] 188 Cork
- [ ] 189 Stephens
- [ ] 190 Hampson
- [ ] 191 Browning
- [ ] 192 John
- [ ] 193 Trent
- [ ] 194 Barry
- [ ] 195 Dailey

- [ ] 196 Hampson
- [ ] 197 Summers
- [ ] 198 Hunter
- [ ] 199 Roberts
- [ ] 200 Lloyd
- [ ] 201 Starr
- [ ] 202 Hampson
- [ ] 203 Browning
- [ ] 204 Carroll
- [ ] 205 Maxam
- [ ] 206 Manning
- [ ] 207 Windham

$1.95 each

- [ ] 208 Halston
- [ ] 209 LaDame
- [ ] 210 Eden
- [ ] 211 Walters
- [ ] 212 Young

- [ ] 213 Dailey
- [ ] 214 Hampson
- [ ] 215 Roberts
- [ ] 216 Saunders
- [ ] 217 Vitek

- [ ] 218 Hunter
- [ ] 219 Cork
- [ ] 220 Hampson
- [ ] 221 Browning
- [ ] 222 Carroll

- [ ] 223 Summers
- [ ] 224 Langan
- [ ] 225 St. George

___ #226 SWEET SECOND LOVE, Hampson

___ #227 FORBIDDEN AFFAIR, Beckman

___ #228 DANCE AT YOUR WEDDING, King

___ #229 FOR ERIC'S SAKE, Thornton

___ #230 IVORY INNOCENCE, Stevens

___ #231 WESTERN MAN, Dailey

___ #232 SPELL OF THE ISLAND, Hampson

___ #233 EDGE OF PARADISE, Vernon

___ #234 NEXT YEAR'S BLONDE, Smith

___ #235 NO EASY CONQUEST, James

___ #236 LOST IN LOVE, Maxam

___ #237 WINTER PROMISE, Wilson

━━ ━━ ━━ ━━ ━━ ━━ ━━ ━━ ━━ ━━ ━━ ━━ ━━ ━━ ━━ ━━ ━━ ━━ ━━ ━━

SILHOUETTE BOOKS, Department SB/1

1230 Avenue of the Americas
New York, NY 10020

Please send me the books I have checked above. I am enclosing $_____
(please add 50¢ to cover postage and handling. NYS and NYC residents please
add appropriate sales tax). Send check or money order—no cash or C.O.D.'s
please. Allow six weeks for delivery.

NAME _____

ADDRESS _____

CITY _____ STATE/ZIP _____

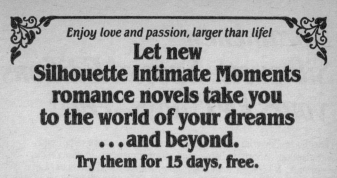

6 brand new
Silhouette Special Editions
yours for 15 days—Free!

For the reader who wants more…more story…more detail and description…more realism…and more romance…in paperback originals, 1/3 longer than our regular Silhouette Romances. Love lingers longer in new Silhouette Special Editions. Love weaves an intricate, provocative path in a third more pages than you have just enjoyed. It is love as you have always wanted it to be—and more —intriguingly depicted by your favorite Silhouette authors in the inimitable Silhouette style.

15-Day Free Trial Offer

We will send you 6 new Silhouette Special Editions to keep for 15 days absolutely free! If you decide not to keep them, send them back to us, you pay nothing. But if you enjoy them as much as we think you will, keep them and pay the invoice enclosed with your trial shipment. You will then automatically become a member of the Special Edition Book Club and receive 6 more romances every month. There is no minimum number of books to buy and you can cancel at any time.